THE EARLY BIRDS

BOOKS BY ARCH WHITEHOUSE

Wings of Adventure
Hell in the Heavens
Hell in Helmets
Crime on a Convoy Carrier
The Real Book of Airplanes
Fighters in the Sky
The Years of the Sky Kings
Tank
The Years of the War Birds
Bombers in the Sky
Combat in the Sky
Subs and Submariners
Adventure in the Sky
Squadrons of the Sea
Billy Mitchell
Action in the Sky
Legion of the Lafayette
Amphibious Operations
Decisive Air Battles of World War I
John J. Pershing
Heroes and Legends of World War I
Espionage and Counterespionage
Squadron 44
Frank Luke
The Early Birds

THE EARLY BIRDS

The Wonders and Heroics of the
First Decades of Flight

Arch Whitehouse

1965
Doubleday & Company, Inc.   Garden City, New York

DEDICATED TO

All members of the Early Birds, those bold adventurers who pioneered the skyways and set the pattern of a glorious history.

Contents

Lists of Illustrations

Introduction

On Saturday, April 6, 1844, Edgar Allan Poe, poet and novelist, arrived in New York from Philadelphia, hungry, and destitute, with but $4.50 in his pocket. With him was his wife Virginia who was seriously ill with tuberculosis. The author was not an outstanding physical specimen either, for precarious health and irregular habits had taken a severe toll, and though he had held important literary posts and was the renowned author of *The Fall of the House of Usher* and *Tales of the Grotesque,* he usually was struggling with poverty. He had few friends, and accepted mere pittances for his articles. But in this instance his child-wife needed care, a warm bed, and nourishing food. Something drastic had to be done.

One week later, April 13, 1844, an Extra edition of the New York *Sun* carried a detailed account of an aerial crossing of the Atlantic Ocean by a party of adventurers, consisting of eight intrepid Englishmen. Needless to state, the report astounded America, and there was an immediate public clamor for further details.

This daring voyage, so the report read, was made in a "flying machine," built and owned by a Mr. Monck Mason of London. Readers with a scientific turn of mind accepted the news with high enthusiasm since many of them already were familiar with Mr. Mason and his aerial exploits. In 1836 he had financed the building of a balloon, and the development of a guide-rope apparatus that, dragging along the earth some 2000 feet below, had enabled the air travelers to carry less ballast, use gas more thriftily, and ascend automatically to pass over mountains in their way. In fact, Mason, together with Charles Green, a noted balloon pilot, and Robert Hollond, had actually flown from London to Weilburg, Germany, a distance of 480 miles, in approximately eighteen hours, one of the greatest feats of aeronautics in the first half of the nineteenth century. It was, therefore, quite understandable that American readers would be eager to learn more of this latest exploit, and were soon making plans to pay high homage to this doughty crew of aerial adventurers.

According to the newspaper account, this transatlantic trip was accomplished in three days, starting on April 6, from Woolwich outside London, and ending at Sullivan's Island near Charleston, South Carolina, on April 9. News of the great event was delayed because it had to be sent by mail from Charleston to New York, but the full details, taken from the joint diary of Messrs. Monck Mason and Harrison Ainsworth, author of *Jack Sheppard*, etc., who was a passenger on the flight, took up the entire front page of the New York newspaper.

The report began as follows:

The great problem is at length solved! The air, as well as the earth and the ocean, has been subdued by science and will become a common and convenient highway for mankind. *The Atlantic has been actually crossed in a Balloon!* and this too without difficulty—without any apparent danger—with thorough control of the machine—and in the inconceivably brief period of seventy-five hours from shore to shore. By the energy of an

agent at Charleston, S.C., we are enabled to be the first to
furnish the public with a detailed account of this most extraordinary voyage which was performed between Saturday, the
6th instant at 11 A.M., and 2 P.M. on Tuesday, the 9th instant;
by Sir Everard Bringhurst; Mr. Osborne, nephew of Lord Bentinck's [Lord William G. Bentinck was a noted sportsman of
that day]; Mr. Monck Mason and Mr. Robert Hollond, the well-
known aeronauts; Mr. Harrison Ainsworth, noted author, and
Mr. William Samuel Henson—with two seamen from Woolwich
—in all, eight persons. The particulars furnished below may be
relied on as authentic and accurate in every respect, as with
slight exception they are copied *verbatim* from the joint diaries
of Mr. Mason and Mr. Ainsworth, to whose politeness our agent
is indebted for much verbal information respecting the balloon
itself, its construction and other matters of interest.

Over the weekend, readers within the circulation area of
the New York *Sun* were agog with the remarkable exploit
and could scarcely wait until Monday's edition to learn
more details, and perhaps gaze on a picture of the remarkable machine and its renowned crew.

Unfortunately, all that greeted their eager interest on that
day was a short report that read: "The mails from the South
last Saturday night not having brought confirmation of the
arrival of the balloon from England, we are inclined to believe the intelligence is erroneous."

Later, it was learned and admitted that the entire tale
was a magnificent fabrication—possibly the greatest hoax
ever perpetrated on the American press—and had come
from the pen of Edgar Allan Poe who had used his renowned imagination to create Mr. Mason's airship *Victoria,*
a "steering balloon," and the full details of the transatlantic
flight to garner some immediate funds to provide care and
shelter for Mrs. Poe.

The world was ripe for this sort of hoax, for man-made
flight was continually in the mind of the public. This Vic-

torian era was to become an age that in the span of a single lifetime was to witness man's triumph over the elements of this age-long conquest. Human progress was gathering momentum and sweeping everything before it. Amid all the glory of Victoria's world, men—and women—were striving to conquer the air. The efforts brought disaster along with success. Henry Cocking lost his life in a parachute accident, but Mrs. George Graham of London, in order to raise money for Cocking's widow, built a balloon she called the *Royal Victoria* and regularly took other ladies aloft for a fee, turning the proceeds over to the desolate widow.

These were the days of lighter-than-air projects, and another Englishman, John Hampton, was intrigued with Cocking's parachute idea, and in 1838 he descended from a balloon that was two miles in the air, and after a drop that lasted thirteen minutes landed safely five miles away from his point of ascent. Two years later Charles Green, who already had the London-to-Germany feat to his credit, announced a bold plan to fly a "sailing balloon" across the Atlantic, so it is easy to see where Edgar Allan Poe first conceived his New York *Sun* hoax. However, after three years of trial and error, Green gave up the idea with the explanation that although he could build and equip a balloon that would stay in the air for three months, the daring of his plan was too much for his financial backers.

Up till then most flying adventures were planned with the hot-air or coal-gas balloon in mind, but there were a few imaginative souls who believed that mechanical—heavier-than-air—flight could be developed if science and engineering would co-operate, and if some suitable engine could be devised to furnish the necessary power. Probably the first machine designed (on paper) to employ such power was introduced by Sir George Cayley, since known as the

"Father of British Aeronautics," who spent much time in drawing up plans for a heavier-than-air machine, combining two sets of circular planes set on either side of the body to provide the lift. Two propellers were to force the machine forward, and the power plant, a small steam engine, was to be mounted inside the "framing" or fuselage. It was to be equipped with an elevator and rudder for lateral and vertical guidance. Cayley, who had had some success with gliders, unfortunately never put his powered machine to an actual test. He might have produced successful mechanical flight some time before 1850, for the Smithsonian Institution in Washington long ago proved its scientific worth with a model built on Cayley's original plans.

The real nucleus for Poe's great fabrication was probably the wide publicity given to William Samuel Henson's "Aerial Steam Carriage" that was designed to fly on regular service between England and India, or China, carrying goods, letters, troops, and passengers. This plan was announced widely in 1843, and the enterprise was made public with the idea of raising funds with which to put the "stupendous project" in operation.

Henson's Aerial Transit Company created a great stir all over the world, being presented as a worthy commercial purpose, an organization to fly a paying airline between Great Britain and China or India. Parliament was asked to provide funds, but at that time England was in the throes of industrial revolution, and the politicians were too involved with the Corn Laws to release public funds for such a haphazard scheme.

William Henson, a lace manufacturer, was associated with a scientist, John Stringfellow; a newspaperman, Frederick Marriott; and a London lawyer, C. E. Columbine. This group sought a charter for a company to establish proof of

Henson's patent that it claimed was "so simple in principle and so perfect in all the ingredients required for complete and permanent success" that many of the details could not be disclosed until protected by further patents.

But the money for the venture was not forthcoming, and Henson and Stringfellow went on by themselves until they had exhausted their own funds. Their machine was a monoplane in design and was to be powered by a 25–30 horsepower steam engine, driving two pusher propellers. It had a wingspread of 150 feet, and the body, or nacelle, carried a three-wheeled undercarriage for take-offs and landings.

Henson actually had developed a small steam engine, weighing ten pounds, that he had used to test small models of his invention. One of these, operated with a clockwork motor, is said to have flown from sixty to eighty feet when tested indoors. Making other trials at his home, and later on a racecourse at Bayswater, outside London, this clever Englishman had varying success and failure. Marriott and Columbine eventually sold their interests in the device, and the newspaperman went to San Francisco and became editor of the San Francisco *News Letter*. Marriott later was interested in the development of dirigible airships.

Henson next formed a company to exploit his "Aeriel," another spring-driven model that was developed into a 40-foot wing-span machine, powered by an engine designed by Stringfellow. This version was not tested until 1847, and the first trials were made at night on Bala Down, chiefly to avoid the caustic comments of derisive onlookers. In this case, however, dew on the grass caused the silken wings to warp, denying the experimenters any hope of success. Henson then gave up the whole idea, turned everything over to Stringfellow, and left England for the United States.

All the publicity and exploitation of Henson's Aerial

Transit Company in turn encouraged many humorous articles in prose and verse. The cartoonists made the most of the possibilities, and another classic hoax was perpetrated on April 1, 1843, when a fictitious Professor Geolls wrote a graphic description of an "Experimental Trip in an Aerial Machine" that was published by the *Glasgow Constitutional*. In this report "Professor Geolls" presented full details of the start, the flight over the River Clyde, an accident caused by the bursting of three steam pipes—and the fall of the aircraft and its passengers into the river. He concluded with a graphic description of their being rescued by a passing steamer.

Surprisingly, the *London Times* copied the Glasgow report verbatim as a true account of an actual happening, and the London editor even ran an editorial to the effect that the details were from the narrative of Professor Geolls himself. This hoax has passed into history as fact and still appears in many standard reference works. Is it any wonder, then, that when the Wright brothers claimed some sixty years later to have flown an engine-powered aircraft from the dunes of Kitty Hawk practically no important publication in the United States would record the event?

But hoax and mishap only added to the universal interest in the possibility of flight. Experimenters and scientists the world over persisted in their quests, despite the warning of Simon Newcomb, astronomer and physicist, who proved by mathematics that mechanical flight was totally impossible. The tinkerers and experimenters would not be talked down or discouraged, and in 1847 Werner von Siemens, a German army officer, announced that he was preparing to build a rocket plane, an aircraft that was to be propelled by charges of gunpowder. Old prints, still available, disclose that this contrivance was built around a boat body set on a wheeled undercarriage, and show warped monoplane wings. The rocket engine, employing charges of gunpowder to furnish the thrust, was mounted inboard. The pilot, wearing a top hat, sat in the stern and guided the machine with a tail assembly that was not far removed from that of any modern light plane. There is no evidence, though, that Siemens ever completed a working model of this device, or that he attempted to fly his invention, but a striking picture of the general idea appeared in the Leipzig *Illustrierten Zeitung* in 1847, which must have impressed many gullible readers that such a machine had been flown.

It was not until the appearance of the British engineer, John Stringfellow, with his series of steam-powered models in 1848 that the possibility of mechanical flight (as opposed to lighter-than-air conquests of the ballooning science) seemed within reach. After W. S. Henson had given up his quest, Stringfellow who had been associated with Henson's Aerial Transit Company, kept at the task, and eventually gave the scientific world its most satisfactory machine.

Stringfellow first redesigned and lightened the steam engine that had been used in earlier models, and then began experimenting with a model of twenty-foot wingspread, powered by twin propellers. This device was launched from a taut starting cable, and when it reached "the point of self-detachment," it gradually rose and flew the length of a long room in Stringfellow's lace factory located at Chard in Somerset.

Enthusiastic over this first example of dynamic flight, recorded in June 1848, a Mr. Ellis offered to provide Stringfellow with a long "covered way" in the Cremorne Gardens, a popular amusement resort of London. There, under outdoor conditions, Stringfellow's model raced along the taut wire and got successfully away despite some obstruction encountered near the end of the cable. According to contemporary accounts, it recovered by inherent stability, and continued on for a distance of 40 feet, or until it came to rest in a restraining canvas at the end of the covered way.

This model, now generally considered the first successful flying model in history, may still be seen with many of its original parts in the Science Museum at South Kensington, London. Stringfellow won some acclaim, but little financial reward, and shortly after the Cremorne Gardens flight he and his son left for an extended program of travel in the United States. He was not heard of again in the aeronautical world until 1868.

Two years before—1866—Stringfellow had listened to a paper on "Aerial Locomotion" delivered by Francis H. Wenham before the Royal Aeronautical Society. An English engineer, Wenham had won the title "Father of the Biplane" for his patent on the first flying machine employing superposed planes. He is also credited with developing the first English light gas engine for air experiments.

Impressed with Wenham's theories, Stringfellow went his countryman one better by designing a triplane around a new light, steam engine. In fact, he entered this engine and two model planes in the First Aeronautical Exhibition of the Royal Aeronautical Society and won a prize of £100 which he used to build a laboratory for further experiments. Though he was now sixty-nine years of age and his eyesight was failing, he devoted the remaining fifteen years of his life to the development of mechanical flight.

During one exhibition at the Crystal Palace in London, Stringfellow's triplane flew at high speed along its wire, and proved that it had sufficient lift to maintain actual flight. In another test staged in the basement of the exhibition building, it was free-flown, and satisfied all who saw the flight that it would fly under its own power anywhere sufficient space could be provided. The engine used in these last experiments is still owned by the Smithsonian Institution in Washington, and a model Stringfellow triplane built around it is on exhibition in the National Museum.

We see, then, that a new epoch of mechanical flight had been opened, and all that was required to give man wings was a suitable engine, one capable of providing the power —and the courage of man to venture into the air and chance this unknown element. Men had ascended in gas-filled balloons. They had passed over wide expanses of water. International boundaries had been crossed, and great heights had been reached, but in all these exploits man had employed the lift of lighter gases held in an envelope; he was moved about the sky by the vagaries of the wind; his own devices and engineering imagination had played no important role. He could only rise from the earth and be carried along by the prevailing wind. He had little or no directional control; he was shunted about by the will of Aeolus.

Ballooning was spectacular, but it was not enough. Man wanted wings, and wings required suitable power. He had the framework, the structural design, and he knew the primary laws of gravity and propulsion. Steam power was not the answer. Fortunately, Germany gave the world Gottlieb Daimler who in 1886 produced an internal-combustion engine, a power plant in which he successfully employed high revolutionary speeds, enabling bulk and weight to be lessened greatly, and the power increased. He also successfully and safely employed mixtures of volatile liquid hydrocarbons or "petrols" as fuel. His engines were first used in motorcars where their inevitable refinement took place, and by 1903 they were available with 60, 80, and even 100 horsepower; at the same time their weight was cut from 88 pounds per horsepower to 20 pounds per horsepower.

Man was ready to spread his wings.

CHAPTER I

There Shall Be Wings

The Written Records • Roger Bacon's Machine • Blanchard's Flying Machine • American Air Efforts • Development of the Parachute • The Inspiration of Cayley

The idea of machines, heavier than air, that should nevertheless sustain themselves in the air by the operation of suitable mechanism, is an obvious deduction from the observation of birds and of flying animals and insects, all of which are vastly heavier than the tenuous medium that supports them. As a consequence the earliest ideas of heavier-than-air flying machines came to man long before the discovery of the balloon. All the myths and apocryphal accounts of flying men of ancient times were founded on one or another of the modifications of the mechanical-bird concept.

The story of man's attempt to rival the bird is as old as the human race itself. From the moment he realized that he was earthbound, he had been pondering on how to clip these bondage chains. Failing to solve the problems of flight by physical means, early man attributed the art to some supernatural power, a skill that might be gained in the world he would reach after death.

Man's thought processes, and the evolution of flight are to be traced through the lagging development of human intelligence, a tortuous course that took him through the Stone Age, the Bronze Age, and the Iron Age until at last into this Air Age with all its majestic possibilities. Such progress stems from the imagination; ideas first drift through the minds of men and are eventually recorded on stone, canvas, or paper. Practical adaptations of these early visual speculations inevitably follow from the minds and hands of scientists and inventors. Much of this documentary evidence has been gathered over a period of five to six hundred years, and it offers the fascinating details of the heroic efforts put on by man to materialize the concepts into definite form.

We are all familiar with the mythology of ancient Greece and Rome, which in turn are antedated by archaeological records going back as far as 3500 B.C. The oldest of the Grecian tales is that of Daedalus and Icarus. Daedalus who built the famed Labyrinth of the Minotaur for King Minos of Crete, eventually lost the favor of the king and was imprisoned in a tower. After escaping from his prison, he fabricated wings of feathers for himself and Icarus, his young son. These wings were secured with thread and fastened on with wax. Daedalus ordered Icarus to fly near him, "neither too high nor too low," but Icarus, fascinated with the thrill of such freedom, soared upward too near the sun which melted the wax. His wings collapsed, and the young boy fell into the sea and was drowned. His father, who had been more careful, buried his son's body and called the land Icaria. Among various artists who have gained fame for their versions of this early drama is Leonardo da Vinci who was a progenitor of the birth of the Air Age.

As far back as 305 B.C. Demetrius Poliorcetes' winged statue, *Victory of Samothrace*, conceived in marble man's hopes for winged flight. Grecian mythology also gives us the winged horse Pegasus, a statue of which can still be seen in the Garden of the Tuileries in Paris. At the time of the discovery of America, Leonardo da Vinci had produced his famous *Annunciation* showing a winged figure before the Virgin Mary. Da Vinci later gave the world its first plans for a flying machine—and a parachute. With his masterpiece *Ganymede* Rembrandt might be accepted as the patron saint of the world's aviators. The painting depicts the immortal story of Ganymede, son of Tros, King of Troy, being borne above the clouds by an eagle to become the cup bearer to Zeus.

Three noted paintings on view at the Metropolitan Museum of Art in New York continue the mythological hope of man's ability to fly. *Oedipus and the Sphinx* offers a winged monster with the head of a beautiful woman. Another, depicting the legend of Perseus coming to the rescue of Andromeda, shows Perseus astride a flying horse. In the third, *St. Michael,* the Spanish artist Zurbarán paints the Archangel, outfitted with feathered wings, triumphing over another figure likewise complete with a set of short-span wings. Could this have been history's first air battle?

On and on, the pages of history afford dozens of such legends. Men pinned their hopes on feathers, birdlike wings, winged sandals, chariots that could fly, and in several instances they put their trust in teams of doves, peacocks, eagles, or swans harnessed to draw their heavenly equipages. The first Biblical record of human flight appears in the Book of Kings when Elijah was carried up to heaven

from the bank of the Jordan before the wondering eyes of
Elisha, his successor. The text reads, "And behold, there
appeared a chariot of fire, and horses of fire, and parted
them both asunder; and Elijah went up by a whirlwind into
heaven."

The Written Records

This search takes us into the libraries of all human knowledge, and from the world's bookshelves we have a continu-
ous record of man's desire to take on wings. These aspira-
tions are expressed in religion, philosophy, and all shades of
imaginative literature. They appear in the ideographs of
old China, in the hieroglyphics of Egypt, the Arabian sym-
bols on which we have based our alphabet, the Hebraic
scrolls, and the manuscripts of the Greeks and Latins. We
have commented on the flaming chariot of Elijah, but later
on in the Psalms of the Hebrew poets, appear the lines, "He
rode upon a cherub and did fly; yea, he did fly upon the
wings of the wind."

Among the Greeks, Homer told in the *Iliad* how "the
ethereal coursers fly," and all Greek epics of the time gave
the power of flight to their heroes. Aeschylus, Pindar, and
Euripides all discussed methods and possibilities of flight.
The first historian, Herodotus, weighed the possibilities of
heavier-than-air flying, and Euclid and Archimedes, both
great mathematicians, gave much scientific consideration
to the problem. Socrates and Plato indicate that they were
also acquainted with this "question of the times."

King Solomon was not above contriving a vehicle "Whereby one could traverse the air," as is told in *The Kebra
Nagast*, and the oldest of English records concerning flight

is to be found in the history of King Bladud who in 863 B.C., or fifteen years after Carthage was founded, actually attempted to fly from the Temple of Apollo, which he had built in Trinovantum (now London), but he fell upon a church where Westiminster Cathedral now stands, and broke his neck.

This doughty monarch was the father of King Lear. He founded the city of Bath and the first college in England at Stamford. He is also said to have practiced necromancy and taught it throughout the kingdom. Bladud, according to a record penned by Geoffrey of Monmouth in 1147 A.D., fashioned a set of wings of feathers and framework, somewhat after the manner of Daedalus, but the device played him false. He, however, must be considered to be Great Britain's first airman.

This perhaps opened the background for this modern aerial age, for by Bladud's time this aspiration of mankind had been firmly established. In 400 B.C. the Chinese were experimenting with kites, and Archytas of Tarentum was working on his "wooden dove."

Archytas was a noted Greek philosopher, scientist, mathematician, and a general of the army. He devised a wooden dove, or pigeon, which he is said to have made fly by its own power. Some say, in explanation, he was an expert in the art of mechanical balancing of weights that made the movement of the bird in the air a possibility. Gellius, a Latin writer of the second century, suspected that Archytas had employed a lamp or a fire within the bird's body that may have produced such a forcible rarefaction of the air that it became what we would term a gas. Other views suggest that he had some power contrivance within the body that pointed the way toward the internal combustion engine of the present time.

Archytas may be considered to have dealt with the heavier-than-air problem, unless he used a wood lighter than any known today. One historian has suggested that the Greek scientist may have used goldbeater's skin, and inflated it with lighter-than-air gas; if so, he was the first to employ the lighter-than-air principle in the Occidental world.

Roger Bacon's Machine

More than seven hundred years ago an English friar, scientist, and philosopher, Roger Bacon, predicted the possibility of artificial flight. He was one of the earliest students at Oxford University where he first took his M.A. degree. From there he went to Paris where he also received an M.A. certificate. He wrote and lectured in Latin, mainly on metaphysical subjects, and in his early life was most interested in physical science.

His scientific ideas were far in advance of the times, and in 1268, at the request of Pope Clement IV, he wrote a World Encyclopedia. Two years later he produced a still more exhaustive compendium of human knowledge. As a result, Bacon was arrested and brought before Jerome de Ascoli, Minister General of the Franciscan order, to answer the charge of circulating heretical doctrines in Paris. Bacon was found guilty, and this man whose chief interest had been the glorification of the Church, spent the next fifteen years of his life in prison. He was not released until the Minister General died. Roger Bacon lived only one year more.

During his incarceration Bacon continued his writings, and in one treatise made it plain that he believed man was

capable of flight. Along this line, some interesting detail is
found in an English book titled, *The Mirror of Alchemy,* in
which Bacon's work was first printed in his native language.
One passage reads:

And first of all by the figuration of Art itself: There may be
made instruments of navigation without men to row in them:
as huge ships to brooke the Sea, only with one man to steer
them, which shall sail far more swiftly than if they were full
of men. And Chariots that shall move with unspeakable force,
without any living creature to stirre them: such as the crooked
Chariots are supposed to have been, wherein in old time they
used to fight, yes instruments to fly withall, so that one sitting
in the middle of the instrument, and turning an Engine [crank],
by which the wings being artificially composed may beat the
air after the manner of a flying bird.

Moreover instruments may be made wherewith men may walk
on the bottom of the sea or rivers without bodily danger, which
Alexander the Great used, to the end he might behold the secrets
of the seas, as the Ethick Philosopher reporteth: and these have
been made not only in times past, but even in our days. And it
is certain that there is an instrument to fly with, which I never
saw, nor know any man that has seen it, but I full well know by
name the learned man invented the same.

The above, taken from the quaint Chaucerian text of *The
Mirror of Alchemy,* clearly predicts not only heavier-than-
air flight, but the automobile, the steamship, and the submarine.

The mist is clearing, and we are reaching the dawn of the
scientific era in man's ancient struggle to reveal the mys-
teries of the air. By 1490, two years before Columbus was to
prove the earth is round, Leonardo da Vinci was introduc-
ing his designs and plans for mechanical flight, and the
prospects of the aerial lifesaver, the parachute.

The artist who painted *The Last Supper, Mona Lisa,* and
many other notable canvases, had made human flight the

preoccupation of his long career, and probably his last major effort was a portfolio of sketches of his imaginative flying machines.

It was Da Vinci who first cried, "There shall be wings!" and added, "If the accomplishment be not for me, 'tis for some other." Long a devoted student of nature and basically an outdoorsman, the noted artist filled a large sketch book with details of the mechanics of bird flight. He turned out dozens of models of flying machines, and probably tested them out, but none ever satisfied him, and he died before his agile mind could produce the vital secret.

When Providence links art and science in one man we find that that man can not only visualize great scientific theories, but he can present them graphically on paper for other scientists to study or criticize. Leonardo devised a helicopter and a primary idea for the parachute. All this, and his sketches and observations, seem to have been hidden for nearly three hundred years, but, fortunately, most of them can now be seen in the Library of Milan, and several models of his "flying machine," created from his original drawings are on view at the National Museum in Washington, D.C.

Speaking of parachutes that have had an important role in the development of the aeroplane, a Venetian, Fausto Veranzio, according to some historians, made in 1607 or 1617 what is believed to be the first successful descent by such means. His parachute, a square device of sailcloth spread over a light framework, was remarkably like the device drawn originally by Da Vinci. Veranzio, dangling by four cords tied to the corners of the framework, apparently jumped off a tall tower and landed safely below.

The first man actually to attempt human flight with a mechanical device was a French locksmith by the name of

Besnier. In 1678 this inventive man created a rather simple glider-type flying machine that consisted of two rods pivoted on his shoulders. At both ends of each rod were fastened small V-type planes, and these were actuated by Besnier's hands and feet, either for gliding or to provide flight propulsion.

According to some accounts, Besnier claimed to have launched himself from the roof of his home, and to have flown over a barn and landed on another roof. Other reports have it that he flew across a river. At any rate, his story was so convincing he sold his device to an itinerant showman who was killed while trying to give his first professional exhibition.

Strangely enough, in 1751 an engraving appeared in an English publication known as *The Scribleriad*, together with satirical verse by Richard Cambridge, purporting to depict the first aerial race in which a Briton and a German meet before an enthusiastic audience seated in a broad meadow. The English contestant was equipped with feathered wings, but the German is shown flying with a set exactly like those devised by Besnier about seventy-five years before. During the contest, the Englishman's wings collapsed, and to save himself from defeat, he reached out and grasped the foot of his German opponent and they both fell to the turf; in that way the Englishman had upheld the honor of his country. Perfidious Albion, again!

Blanchard's Flying Machine

In 1781 a new figure takes the stage. This was François Blanchard, a Frenchman, who in that year designed and built a flying machine based on the ornithopter principle. This device was known as the "Vaisseau-Volant," and a detailed report of it appeared in the *Journal de Paris*. An illustrator, Martinet, produced a set of four colored engravings of the invention which are still extant.

Blanchard explained, "It is not the material or form of wings which causes flight, but the volume and celerity of movement which should be as rapid as possible."

This flying chariot, invented by this man of humble parentage, and with little formal education, had four great wings that were attached to a light car. The operator sat inside this and operated the wings with hand and foot pedals and levers. This device was never exhibited in public, for Blanchard quickly learned, of course, that he could not move the wings fast enough to get off the ground. His detractors scoffed at his effort, and one member of the Academy of Sciences declared that it would require wings two or three thousand feet long, moved at a speed of three feet per second, for Blanchard to raise himself off the ground and to hover there. Later on, Blanchard applied his winged device to a spherical balloon, and in after years became an important figure in this new science.

But the world was not too interested in heavier-than-air flight, as success and enthusiasm had crowned the art of ballooning. Lighter-than-air gas was more reliable than mechanical wings, and all of Europe was entranced by the developments that followed the Montgolfiers' dramatic proof that a balloon could be employed in aerial navigation. That memorable event took place in 1783 when a linen and paper envelope, 110 feet in circumference, inflated with hot air, rose to a height of 6000 feet; a triumph that thrilled all Europe. More than 300,000 people witnessed this amazing event, but when a short time later F. Pilâtre de Rozier, head of the French Royal Museum, and his friend the

Marquis d'Arlandes made the world's first human balloon ascent, the gas bag took the prime position in the race for the conquest of the air. A man willing to make a balloon ascent was welcome everywhere, and aerial history in volume after volume was being written with a high-speed pen to relate the thrilling events.

Nothing of importance is recorded in the heavier-than-air field until 1784 when a Frenchman, usually listed as M. Gérard, attempted to devise a flying machine in which birdlike wings were to be flapped by some mechanical power; but there was no suitable motive power available, and M. Gérard has left only a primitive drawing to explain his effort.

All this was quickly forgotten when Dr. John Jeffries of Boston, Massachusetts, became the first passenger on an aerial flight across the English Channel. This world-shaking event was carried out by the aforementioned François Blanchard, backed by Dr. Jeffries who, in 1779, was working in London with the noted British surgeon, Dr. John Hunter.

Dr. Jeffries financed Blanchard to the extent of $35,000 and then paid an additional $3500 for his fare as a passenger. The flight, carried out in 1785, was made in a spherical balloon supporting a wicker basket that bore a pair of light oarlike wings with which it was hoped to augment the propulsion of the wind. This flight was later proclaimed as the greatest feat of the century.

About one o'clock in the afternoon of a wintry day, January 7, 1785, the huge gas-filled balloon with Blanchard and Jeffries in the basket took off from above the white cliffs of Dover. A light breeze came up and the big bag drifted slowly southeast, and they began their voyage, passing over a great crowd on the cliffs, and as many more in all sorts of water craft.

Blanchard was uneasy, being far from satisfied with the arrangements. Before taking off, he had tried to prevent Dr. Jeffries from accompanying him, but the American insisted on carrying out the conditions of their contract. He was so determined to make the flight he agreed that if the balloon failed to rise—and if all other ballast failed—he would jump overboard into the Channel.

The two aeronauts carried but thirty pounds of sand ballast, and by the time they were well out over the Channel all of this had been jettisoned to keep them in the air. By 2:30 P.M. the coast of France was in full view, but again they were descending too fast for safety. They had lost about one fourth of their gas through leakage and the necessary valving to stay at their planned level. To keep from landing in the water Blanchard and Jeffries next tossed some of their food supplies overboard, such as biscuits and apples. When this sacrifice did not improve their altitude they tossed over the winged oars, in fact all removable apparatus. Still the balloon would not rise so they removed the basket lining and useless ornaments. Next to go was the anchor and hanks of valuable rope.

"Nothing seemed to help," Dr. Jeffries related later, "so we began to strip ourselves. Blanchard first tossed away his extra coat and surtout [another form of the greatcoat]; and I then discarded my only coat. Blanchard next sacrificed his light coat and trousers, and by this time I was so concerned, and being a physician, I suggested that we gag ourselves and vomit up what food we had already eaten, but this was not necessary. We put on and adjusted our cork jackets and prepared for a plunge into the sea.

"We could see the French coast plainly and we were just

preparing to clamber up into the rigging when I noticed the mercury in our barometer was again falling, and looking around, I noticed that we were rising and that the pleasant view of France was becoming clearer with every minute."

By 3:00 P.M. they had ascended higher than at any time during their flight and were certain of reaching their goal. They passed over high ground between Cape Blanc and Blackness near Calais and floated over the forest at Guînes at so low an altitude they were able to snatch at branches of trees and thereby bring the balloon to earth. They had been in the air for more than two hours.

Blanchard and Jeffries deflated the balloon, and joyous people escorted them to Calais where, according to the oft-told tale, the gates had to be opened for them as it was well past midnight when they reached the French city.

This momentous event aroused the world. The borders of a country had been crossed by air for the first time in history. Geographic frontiers no longer stood, and the seas no longer were barriers. Soldiers and sailors wondered where this would end, and some asked, "Will the human race destroy itself with its scientific genius, or will it ultimately unite itself into a great human brotherhood?"

Both France and the United States shared a notable victory in this remarkable exploit, and great throngs hailed Blanchard and Dr. Jeffries with an ovation "fit for emperors." In fact, Louis XVI of France awarded Blanchard 12,000 francs and an annual pension of 1200 francs. A monument in their honor was erected later to mark the spot of their historic landing near Calais.

The Blanchard-Jeffries flight was the forerunner, unfortunately, of the first tragedy of air transportation. J. F. Pilâtre de Rozier, the first man actually to sail in the air, was killed in a fall in a burning balloon on June 15, 1785, while attempting to cross the English Channel from France to England. His passenger, a M. Romain, was also killed. De Rozier, who was twenty-eight years of age, had just become engaged to an English girl, Susan Dyer, who was watching the flight when the balloon burst into flames at about 3000 feet. She is said to have been prostrated by the catastrophe and died of a broken heart eight days later.

American Air Efforts

During all these years no American had a major role in the development of air transport, though some chauvinistic historians have claimed that the first air voyage in the Western Hemisphere was made by two Americans, Rittenhouse and Hopkinson, in December 1785 at Philadelphia, but there is no authentic record of such a flight. Later, a James Wilcox, a carpenter, was declared to be America's first aeronaut, but again there is no reliable evidence of this man's aerial activities.

It fell to the lot of François Blanchard, who came to the United States after his celebrated crossing of the English Channel, to make the first balloon ascent in America. This event occurred on January 9, 1793, at Philadelphia and was witnessed by President George Washington who signed all documents relating to the flight.

This was a remarkable period in American scientific history. Eli Whitney perfected the cotton gin. A few years before John Fitch had built a commercial boat, propelled by steam, with which he operated a line on the Delaware River. The inventor of the telegraph, Samuel F. B. Morse, was about two years old; Benjamin Franklin had died three years before (1790). The first American to fly in the Western Hemisphere was Charles Ferson Durant, scientist, naturalist, astonomer, scholar, poet, inventor, and aeronaut, to list a few of his skills. On September 9, 1830, he made an ascent in a balloon from Castle Garden (the Battery) in New York City that was witnessed by 20,000 people. Two hours later, about 4:30 P.M., less than twenty persons were astonished to see Durant land safely near South Amboy, New Jersey. Durant made eleven other balloon ascents over the ensuing years, and on one occasion drifted out over the Atlantic, fell into the ocean and was saved by his "gum-elastic" life preserver.

But another American, whose name seldom appears in the records of our aeronautical accomplishments, was John Wise of Philadelphia who was called the "Patriarch of American Aeronauts." Wise made 440 balloon ascensions in scores of cities and towns all over the United States. In fact, he had been ballooning for more than fourteen years when gold was discovered in California in 1849. His first ascent was from Ninth and Green streets of his home city on May 2, 1835. In this instance he was assisted by Professor J. K. Mitchell of the University of Pennsylvania who helped inflate the bag. They used hydrogen in a twenty-eight-foot sphere made of varnished muslin. Wise later adopted a form of oiled silk, but discovered that when this material was folded for packing, the oil "burned" holes along the folds, so he returned to using cambric muslin.

In October 1837 Wise made an exhibition ascension that was witnessed by the Indian chiefs, Black Hawk and Keokuk. The Philadelphian assumed that the two red men would be impressed by his feat, and was astonished when Black Hawk said, "That is nothing. I saw it done, along with President Jackson, in New York in 1833." The Indian chief was telling the truth, for he had witnessed one of Charles Durant's flights in New York City.

During the Mexican War in 1845 Wise volunteered to act as a balloon observer, offering his services to Secretary of War William L. Marcy, and suggesting that the Castle of San Juan de Ullos, considered the key to the defense of Vera Cruz, be bombed. The Secretary did not accept his offer.

John Wise, who had long planned a transatlantic voyage in a balloon, finally took off from Brooklyn in 1873 in a 400,000-cubic-foot capacity balloon that carried a basket, below which was slung a whaleboat. This great adventure ended in New Canaan, Connecticut, four hours after take-off. In a later balloon ascent over Lake Michigan in 1879 Wise was drowned, and thus passed one of America's great aviation personalities.

Development of the Parachute

While most of these events were taking place, other aeronauts were concentrating on the parachute, a device that was to have an important role in the development of the heavier-than-air craft. Da Vinci's contribution, as early as 1490 when he drew plans for a parachute, has been related. Then, as mentioned, early in the seventeenth century Fausto Veranzio was said to have made a successful descent by a parachute device, after jumping off a structural tower. But it was not until 1797 that man actually descended through the clouds from an aircraft in flight and landed safely.

This historic event occurred when André Jacques Garnerin inflated a balloon from which dangled a parachute that had a wicker car hung beneath it. This Frenchman was in college when the Montgolfier brothers made their first balloon flight. He became so interested in the science he neglected his studies, and was threatened with expulsion. When Garnerin was twenty-five years old he espoused the cause of the French Revolution and during a secret mission, ordered by the Committee of Public Safety, was captured by the Austrians in 1795 and held a prisoner of war for more than two years. He was eventually exchanged and returned to Paris where he resumed his main interest —ballooning.

On October 22, 1797, Garnerin ascended from the Parc Monceau in Paris and rose to a height of 3000 feet. There he cut the parachute loose and returned safely to earth. The remarkable feature of this achievement was that the parachute canopy was only eight yards in diameter so that the car and its occupant descended at a dangerous rate and landed heavily. Garnerin was thrown from his seat but suffered only a bruised foot. The aeronaut climbed out, mounted a waiting horse, and carrying a flag over one shoulder, galloped back to the patrons still gathered in the Parc Monceau.

Five years later, on September 21, 1802, Garnerin repeated this performance from Grosvenor Square in London. This time he allowed his balloon to rise to 8000 feet before cutting his parachute loose. Ten minutes later he landed near St. Pancras Church.

The continued success of balloon flight, and the many possibilities for its application to trade, transport, and even war, did not discourage completely the proponents of mechanical flight. One of the most determined was Jacob Degen, a Vienna clockmaker who held the public's eye and interest for more than five years with his *Flugmaschine*, another birdlike affair that was built around a pair of umbrella-shaped wings covered with taffeta. The material was attached loosely to simulate the free action of bird feathers when the wings were beaten by human power.

After five years of trial and error at home, Degen was encouraged to take his invention to Paris in 1812. He had claimed to have risen to a height of 54 feet in Vienna in 1809—in the presence of a large assemblage of people. On the strength of this assertion, he was given considerable publicity, but the aviation writers of the day neglected to mention that Degen had been aided by a small balloon that, according to its capacity, accounted for at least 90 pounds of the 160 needed to get him and his machine into the air.

When Degen was questioned in Paris about this auxiliary lift, he explained that the balloon had nothing to do with the ability of his machine to gain height and maintain headway, but that he had adopted it to lighten his efforts and to give some aid in maintaining equilibrium in the air. But he never attempted to fly without the lighter-than-air accessory.

The Viennese clockmaker gave a number of exhibitions in Paris, but on each trial he and his invention were blown away by the wind, and no mechanical flight was produced. After three such failures, the onlookers became unruly, derisive, and finally turned on Degen, broke up his machine and beat him unmercifully. He was laughed out of the city as an impostor.

Another enterprising effort was made around 1810 when a British portrait painter, Thomas Walker, a native of Hull, conceived and drew plans for a mechanical bird. This device was never constructed, but the best that came from it was his book, *A Treatise Upon the Art of Flying by Me-*

chanical Means, that was a best seller for more than twenty years and ran into several editions, being better known than its author.

Fifteen years passed before a new effort was made to solve the problems of mechanical flight. This time it was an Italian inventor, Vittorio Sarti, who devised a helicopter design in 1825, and produced a double air-screw affair in which the vanes of this windmill were hinged and could flap, presumably setting up forward motion. But like so many amateurs of this science, he had little hope of success until a suitable lightweight engine could be produced, because no arrangement of cranks and levers could increase the available manpower sufficiently to provide the mechanical propulsion, whether in the helicopter or ornithopter design.

The Inspiration of Cayley

The science of heavier-than-air flight had its greatest boost with the arrival on the scene of Sir George Cayley (1773–1857), "Father of British Aeronautics," who made the world's first scientific experiments with gliders, and first roused interest in an aeronautical society. He was an inspiring figure in aerial navigation for more than half a century.

When the Montgolfiers made their first balloon flight, Sir George was but nine years of age, and his mind never relinquished its interest in the science. He experimented with an aerial top when he was twenty-three, and began investigating the properties of air and power necessary for flight, and he was the first to point out that it would be impossible to fly unless a sufficiently light engine, that did not then exist, were invented. In this, he forecast the internal combustion engine.

In aeronautical science Cayley was far ahead of his time, and he stated publicly in 1810 that he could construct a balloon "that should carry twenty passengers at twenty miles an hour," a statement which he had the undoubted ability to fulfill. This keen interest led to his attempting to form a national aeronautical society in 1837, but he was unsuccessful.

Cayley's first writings on mechanical flight appeared in 1810, and his last in 1854. He designed a model glider as early as 1804, but for many years devoted his efforts toward the construction of a dirigible. In his grasp of the basic principles of the problem he was, to some extent, the real pioneer of the rigid airship. He, perhaps, was the first man to suggest the division of the airship frame into separate compartments, and the necessity of bracing the structure to maintain its shape. He will never gain fully his place in the rigid airship field, as the bulk of the early honors were unconditionally heaped on Count Ferdinand von Zeppelin. But history is clear in its proof that all of Count Zeppelin's early failures were due to continued structural weaknesses; weaknesses that had to be pointed out by Dr. Hugo Eckener.

To appreciate fully Cayley's contribution to the science of mechanical flight, it should be stated that he also made careful calculations of the lift and motor power required, the weight of the fabric to be used, and the possible methods of propelling any airship. He was the first man to study the problems from the scientific and engineering points of view. His notebooks are eloquent testimony to his many ideas. In them are diagrams and calculations of bird flight, notes of experiments in aerodynamics with a whirling arm to find the resistance and lift of a flat plane—the first known tests of that kind. He made a study of streamlined forms, notes on the first attempt to investigate the law of the center of pressure, and many other knotty problems bearing on flight.

Cayley must be credited with the development of plans for the first heavier-than-air flying machine, the design of which was published in *Mechanics' Magazine* in April 1843. This machine, mentioned in our introduction, only required suitable power to produce the necessary lift and forward propulsion. This has been proven by tests made with a model built on Cayley's original plans.

But it was John Stringfellow who first produced a model aeroplane, powered with an engine, that would fly. Stringfellow had been apprenticed to the lace trade in Nottingham, England, and in his early years showed rare mechanical ability. Born in 1799, he had left his original master by 1830 and opened his own lace factory at Chard in Gloucestershire. Once that project was in operation and running, Stringfellow turned his attention to mechanical flight and joined with W. S. Henson who was interested in power-driven models.

Henson soon gave up in despair, but by 1848 Stringfellow produced his large engine-driven model that was the first machine of its kind to fly under engine power. His one-half horsepower steam engine, including water and fuel, weighed 16½ pounds. In a later model, raised to one horsepower and capable of sustaining a pressure of 500 pounds to the square inch, Stringfellow cut the weight to about 40 pounds. He ended this quest for power by perfecting a one-horsepower steam engine that weighed less than 14 pounds. Thus, it can be seen that Stringfellow was on the track of suitable power, even though he had to be content with steam for propulsion. He died December 13, 1883, almost twenty years to the day before the Wright brothers made their historic flight at Kitty Hawk.

CHAPTER II

The Goal of the Gliders

Life with the Lilienthals • The Search Continues •
Was Ader the First? • The Perils of Pilcher • Hiram
Maxim's Marvelous Machine • The Saga of Santos-
Dumont • Lanchester and Prandtl • The Contribution
of Chanute • The Trials of Mr. Montgomery

In these days of intercontinental ballistic missiles,
supersonic bombers, and jet transports that span oceans in
a few hours, it may be difficult to consider the uncertain
probings of the early air experimenters with anything other
than mild amusement, or to award them any particular
value, but their eventual impact on aviation history cannot
be ignored or denied. There would have been no Wright
biplane, no war in the air during 1914–18, no thrilling
transoceanic flights, no intercontinental air lines without
these early efforts. Fumbling and impractical as many of
these projects seem, they all contributed to the great conquest, a quest that would not accept defeat. While the
world suffered crisis after crisis, and the foundations of
many nations were being relaid, while unsound economic

and false social structures were to invite political upheavals and collapse, there were definite examples of sounder scientific principles in the minds of men by which the new air age was to arise.

Wars erupt, and devastate, but, nevertheless, do contribute to the sciences. A young German military observer, Count Ferdinand von Zeppelin, was following the fortunes of President Lincoln's Union Army, and was fascinated to see a captive balloon being used for military observation. Henry T. Coxwell, British aeronaut, was suggesting the use of balloons for military purposes, and the Duke of Argyll was advocating more interest in heavier-than-air flights. The first Aeronautical Exposition was held in London, and Thomas Moy was working on a flying machine "capable of 150 mph." John Erickson was developing his ironclad warship; Richard J. Gatling had invented a machine gun, and Alfred B. Nobel had introduced a new explosive he called dynamite.

Awaiting the development of a suitable engine, the aeronautical scientists of the nineteenth century had to be content with dozens of interesting, and ofttimes daring efforts. Most of them were based on the standard attempt to reproduce bird flight by light wings, pivoted on a framework or harness fixed to the shoulders or waist of the operator.

Dr. W. Miller of London produced an impressive ornithopter device in 1843 by which he hoped to simulate bird flight through simple levers and cables worked by his hands and feet. The plans, still in a London collection, show a well-thought-out device, but it is not known whether Dr. Miller ever got off the ground.

M. Letur, a French aeronaut, devised a glider-parachute apparatus with which he was taken into the air by a balloon that was piloted by a man named Adama. They ascended from the aforementioned Cremorne Gardens in London, and when Letur was released from the balloon he performed several daring evolutions in his descent but was thrown against some trees and fatally injured.

In that same year, 1854, another Frenchman, M. Breant, designed a wing-flapping contrivance that was included in Octave Chanute's *Progress in Flying Machines,* written in 1894.

A sea captain from the Brittany coast, Jean-Marie le Bris, built what he called an "Artificial Albatross" in 1855, and made a determined attempt to imitate that powerful sea bird. The body, made of light wood, had the form of a dory and carried hinged wings with a 23-foot spread. The wings which were light ash were covered with canton flannel and stressed with steel wires. An arrangement of cords and pulleys were supposed to make the wings flap.

At any rate, for its first trial flight Le Bris arranged to have the machine hauled from his yard and along a public road on a flat cart to his aerodrome. Once on the highway the horse went into an animated trot, and the equipage is said to have moved so fast Le Bris's artificial bird began to take off with the inventor sitting in the boat. During this unexpected ascent a rope that was dangling from the machine became entangled around the body of the driver, and, to prevent an accident, Pilot Le Bris had to guide his "Albatross" back to the bed of the cart, ending the flight. Le Bris did not try to fly his machine again.

In 1864 two Russians engineers, Struve and Telescheff, built a huge flying machine that had five sets of wings. The device created controversy throughout Europe, and several farsighted editors were inspired to say, "The nation that conquers the air will rule the world." Thus, when Struve and Telescheff presented their unorthodox device, scientists began new tests and experiments to keep up with this Russian advance.

Although five wings fitted to a long flat body may have been impressive, the two Russians were as handicapped as they would have been with a single set. They had sound aeronautical ideas, but they had no power plant to put the device into the air. The "quintiplane" was never tested.

The word "aviation" probably was coined by the French aeronaut Gabriel de la Landelle who, in 1863, designed what he called a "Steam Air Liner." He employed the air-screw idea as applied to the helicopter. Its most interesting feature was a boat-shaped body from which two broad monoplane wings extended. Elaborate rudder-elevator assemblies were mounted fore and aft, and power was to be supplied by a steam engine that would twirl two sets of helicopter vanes which were fitted on what looked like two ship's masts. In addition, above these vanes, two umbrella parachutes were mounted, that were to be carried folded, and opened only during emergencies. A pusher propeller was run off the auxiliary shaft to furnish forward propulsion. The boiler and engine frame were made of aluminum, and the steam cylinders of bronze.

To continue their work in the heavier-than-air field, Landelle and two of his friends, the Vicomte de Ponton d'Amecourt and Felix Tournachon, known in the aeronautic profession as "Nadar," organized the Société d'Auto-locomotion Aérienne in 1862. Two years later this was known as the Société d'Aviation, the first organization to use the name aviation.

It should be inserted here that Jules Verne wrote, and published in 1865, his renowned literary success, *From the Earth to the Moon* in which a great projectile train carried a group of aerial tourists through the ether at great speed and comfort.

Life with the Lilienthals

The German experimenters, the brothers Lilienthal, now stride into the picture. Otto was born May 24, 1848, at Anklam in Pomerania. He entered the Potsdam Technical School in 1864 where he studied engineering. From 1867 to 1870 he was a student at the Berlin Technical Academy, and served as a volunteer in the Franco-Prussian War. On his demobilization he worked in a Berlin machine shop, but by 1880 had his own factory where he invented a light steam engine. In addition he made a specialty of marine signals for which he was awarded a silver medal.

Although professional engineering had taken much of his time, in 1861, while only thirteen years old, Otto experimented with flying machines, and interested his younger brother Gustav in the hobby. Their first efforts took the form of light wings that were fastened to their arms, and by which they attempted to glide by running down a steep hill. Later the two brothers designed a set of wings that were fastened to their backs and moved up and down by arm power.

They had varied success and failure, and Otto realized that in order to enjoy straight, true glides, they would have to know more of the basic problems of flight. He made a scientific study and measurement of bird flight. His experiments revealed that curved wings were more effective than flat surfaces, and he was the first to point out the value and importance of upward currents of air to bird flight.

In 1889 Otto Lilienthal published the results of these many experiments in a pamphlet titled *The Flight of Birds as a Basis for the Art of Flying*. In 1893, following a number of short, jumping glides, he made a series of true gliding flights near Rathenow, and was soon making glides averaging 250 meters at a height of 30 meters, during which attempts he learned the elements of control. In 1894 Otto built a hill near Berlin for his experiments, and then constructed a biplane glider with a movable, horizontal tail. On August 9, 1896, he met with an accident when his device went into a nosedive from a height of 15 meters. He was injured seriously, and died the next day.

About four thousand miles away in the quiet town of Dayton, Ohio, two brothers, reading of Lilienthal's tragic end and of his gliding experiments, were fascinated with the story of his life. They decided that gliding through the air must be equal to the sport of kings, and wondered if it was possible for them to go on from where the German engineer had left off. Orville and Wilbur Wright were sons of a broadminded bishop of the United Brethren of Christ Church who had sparked their interest in mechanical flight by presenting them with a toy "helicoptere," a gift he had purchased at one of the church's conventions.

The Wright brothers read everything they could find on the art of flying. The local and nearby libraries had little to offer, however, so in May of 1899 Wilbur appealed to Assistant Secretary Richard Rathbun of the Smithsonian Institution in Washington for help and suggestions. At that time Dr. Samuel P. Langley, Director and Secretary of the Institution, had himself made several aeronautical experiments, and had succeeded in building a power-driven model that flew. Dr. Langley later built and attempted to fly a full-sized man-carrying machine, but he was not so fortunate in this advanced field. As history relates, the two bicycle mechanics of Dayton, Ohio, who had written to Washington for information on aeronautics, were the experimenters who gave the world the first successful engine-powered, heavier-than-air aeroplane.

The Search Continues

One hundred years had passed since the Montgolfiers had inflated the balloon with which they originated lighter-than-air flight, and two generations of pioneers had come and gone. Balloons were used in the historic Siege of Paris. The first airmail was established in the same conflict, and, wonder of wonders, the first aerial battle was fought when a balloon crew that was drifting back from Tours to Paris met a German balloon at a height of 10,000 feet. The German aeronaut opened fire with a rifle, but the French balloon captain, none other than Felix Tournachon, shot his way out of the predicament and landed his craft safely in Paris.

Balloons continued to dominate the scene, and when a Belgian shoemaker by the name of De Groof invented a "beating-wing" glider-parachute in 1874, he had to call on a balloonist to take his craft into the air. Failing to obtain such aid in Brussels or Paris, De Groof went to London and induced a British aeronaut, a Mr. Simmons, to take him and his device into the air. This effort took place at the Cremorne Gardens, and when aloft at about 1000 feet, the Belgian cut his glider-parachute loose.

On his first attempt (June 29, 1874) De Groof's machine behaved perfectly, and he returned safely to earth. A week later, on a second venture, he cut loose again, but the wings collapsed immediately and the Belgian fell to earth like a plummet and was killed.

A new ray of hope pierced the gloom when Thomas Moy,

an engineer and a member of the Royal Aeronautical Society, claimed in 1875 to be the first man to "demonstrate the possibility of flying by steam power." Moy was a practical man who had been converted from the lighter-than-air field to a search for a powerful aircraft, and he honestly believed he could design a lightweight steam engine that would provide the necessary power for a successful heavier-than-air flight.

One of his theories was based on what he considered fundamentals. "There is no perceptible pressure on an object moved slowly through the air," he argued, "but there is immense pressure if it be moved fast." On this premise Moy aimed for a flying speed of 150 miles per hour. Aided by R. E. Shill, Moy built an "Aerial Steamer," set on a tricycle undercarriage. It was a monoplane in general design, its chief feature being dual propellers that were turned by a 3-horsepower steam engine. The whole device weighed 120 pounds and in its first test along a board track set up at the Crystal Palace in London, the machine lifted itself several inches above the test track. From all accounts Moy's plane attained a speed of 12 miles per hour with the 6-foot propellers turning at 550 revolutions per minute, but apparently the test was not satisfactory to the group of authoritative witnesses. Here again can be seen the fallacy of attempting powered flight with an engine incapable of high revolutionary speeds.

About 1876 a New Yorker by the name of W. J. Lewis designed an odd-looking model that he claimed to have flown successfully and which he hoped to convert to a full-scale apparatus and fly from New York to Philadelphia and return at a speed of a hundred miles per hour. A drawing of this invention appeared in Leslie's Weekly, December 30, 1876, but there is no record of such a machine being built.

The contrivance was to be set on a boxcar-like body. Two birdlike wings sprouted from the sides of this compartment, and along the top, fore and aft, was a long lattice structure above which sprouted two sets of helicopter screws and a rear-area rudder. A forward portion of this lattice frame was tilted down at a 45-degree angle, and at the nose of this were two contra-rotating propellers.

This Rube Goldberg type of contrivance may have been the inspiration for John T. Trowbridge, New England poet and author who in 1880 published his famous *Darius Green and His Flying Machine,* giving a new name to the English language that was applied to all "crack-brained" inventors who believed they could fly, and tried to do it. They all were Darius Greens.

By 1880 Thomas A. Edison had turned his inventive talents to flying, chiefly at the behest of James Gordon Bennett, publisher of the New York *Tribune,* who established the Gordon Bennett international trophies for yachting, automobile racing, and aeronautical contests. Bennett had given Edison a thousand dollars to make some experiments in flying, and with this financial encouragement Edison tried a basic helicopter, powered by an engine that was actuated by guncotton, an explosive made from stock-ticker paper and ignited by an electric spark.

Edison explained later: "I got good results, but burned one of my men pretty badly and even singed some of my own hair, and we didn't go much further. I guess my helicopter was not light enough.

"But I knew it was only a matter of continuing the experiment, and I reported to Mr. Bennett that when an engine could be made that would weigh only three or four pounds to the horsepower produced, the helicopter would be a success. I believed that it would be the best method and the most likely to be commercially successful. I have not changed my mind, but I have had to wait a long time."

In later experiments Edison demonstrated that plane surfaces propelled through the air rapidly would rise and sustain weight. The difficulty was to get an engine so light in proportion to its power output that it would lift itself *and* a flying machine. Such an engine did not exist in 1880—and Mr. Edison wisely turned his genius to fields of investigation more likely to produce immediate results. But the news that Thomas Edison was experimenting with mechanical flight aroused great interest in Europe, and a French artist, M. Dieuaide, who was also a patent attorney and secretary of the French Aeronautical Society, produced in 1880 a print of "Edison's Flying Ship which is to tour the World."

Mr. Edison denied that his ideas had reached such a stage, and it was admitted that M. Dieuaide had designed this flying ship on the theory of Edison's known aeronautical views. The ship in question had a long narrow enclosed cabin, two sets of monoplane wings set in tandem, and a smaller pair set well forward, obviously for horizontal control. A fish-tail rudder was attached to the stern.

In the last decade before the final breakthrough by the Wright brothers, scientists of England, Germany, France, the United States, and Italy were within reach of the solution of the age-old search, and all were feverishly developing new principles.

By empirical methods Horatio Phillips of England had gone more deeply into the problem of correct wing sections than any previous inventor, and he later produced slatlike multiplane models of extraordinary lifting capacity. A French engineer, Victor Tatin, gave all aviation enthusiasts a new surge of inspiration when his model twin-screw monoplane, powered by a tube of compressed air, developed a speed of 18 miles an hour, rose into the air and flew a distance of 50 feet. Tatin never had the money to build a full-sized machine, but he was employed by the Clement-Bayard firm in France, a company that played an important role in the development of both nonrigid airships and biplanes.

A compressed-air motor provided the power for a model monoplane devised by Lawrence Hargrave of Australia. The most interesting feature of Hargrave's model was that it had the first successful flapping-wing device since Giovanni Alfonso Borelli, Italian physicist and astronomer, in 1680 promulgated the principle of human flight by flapping wings.

Hargrave, who experimented with flapping-wing models for several years, first powered them with twisted rubber strands attached to their tiny propellers to move them forward. Later he devised a compressed-air motor, using one 1½-inch cylinder. One of these models is still on view in the National Museum in Washington. Though the Australian inventor had succeeded thus far, he soon realized that no engine available at the time was powerful enough to drive a full-scale aircraft based on his flapping-wing design.

Was Ader the First?

The premier position held by the Wright brothers in the history of mechanical flight has never been contested in responsible aeronautical circles, but there have always been small groups of dissenting scientists, or caviling science writers who express divergent opinions concerning who first got off the ground with the aid of mechanical flight.

The long, drawn-out Wright-Langley-Curtiss controversy that will be touched on later, is typical of these arguments.

Clement F. Ader was a French electrical engineer who became well-known for his work on the telephone, has often been held up as the man who first flew a power-driven aeroplane. This feat took place in 1890, and there is reliable evidence that Ader did get several machines off the ground, but he could not control them in the air, and crashed on every attempt. This illustrates how close man was to gaining this great end, as it generally was agreed that man could produce mechanical flight, but by 1890 he had to prove that he was in full control of the operation—regardless of the distance or height he had flown.

Unquestionably, Ader was on the right track, but he was unfortunate in his time brackets. Had he waited a few years for the development of the Daimler engine—and some form of the lateral-control aileron—he might have won the laurel that is now the undisputed honor of the Wright brothers.

From boyhood on, Ader had been interested in the possibility of man-made flight, and as a young man lived for months in the interior of Algeria in Arab clothes so as to study vultures in flight. An inspection of his first *Eole*, and his later model, the *Avion*, show the influence of the bird structure in his designs. The wings are almost replicas of bird wings. Ader spent 2,000,000 francs in his basic experiments, and had to appeal to the French War Department for money.

The *Eole* was a birdlike monoplane, fitted with a tractor propeller forward, and driven by a 40-horsepower engine that weighed 1100 pounds. The wingspan was 46 feet, and the over-all length 21 feet. Its undercarriage had turned-up skids instead of wheels.

The *Eole* was built in great secrecy at the Château d'Armainvilliers near Gretz and was first tested in private before a small group of friends on the grounds of the château. An uninvited artist from *L'Illustration* magazine hid in some bushes and sketched the machine from a distance. This illustration seems to be the only picture extant of this historic aircraft.

Friends who witnessed the initial test testified that Ader had flown a distance of 150 feet, but because of deficient equilibrium had crash-landed, and the machine was destroyed. In fact, Octave Chanute is said to have tried to buy an Ader machine for the sum of $100,000 and have the Wright brothers fly it for him. The Dayton brothers, however, believed their designs were far superior.

Clement Ader built his Number 2 model a year later, and received special permission to try it out on a prepared course of 2400 feet at an Army camp located at Satory. This model must have had wheeled gear, for Ader taxied it over the course several times, and finally flew it a distance of 300 feet, but on this occasion smashed a wing on landing.

His *Avion,* the third and last, was not ready until August 18, 1897, and according to French reports it completed several successful flights that were most encouraging. On the second day, Ader attempted to fly during a violent wind, and the *Avion* was blown over and badly wrecked. The French Army officials who were present, considered these flights to be mere hops, and when the machine crashed on the second day, the French War Department abandoned the project. Ader lived long enough—May 3, 1925—to see the skies "filled with aircraft on peace and war missions," but his work in the science ended with the crash of his *Avion.*

The Perils of Pilcher

The first Englishman to fly a glider successfully was Percy Sinclair Pilcher, a product of Her Majesty's Royal Navy. He was so important in this field that he must be considered a member of the great international trio of glider exponents —Lilienthal of Germany, Chanute of the United States, and Pilcher of Great Britain who contributed so much to the eventual accomplishment of power-driven flight.

Pilcher who was born in 1866, served six years at sea, retired in 1885 and devoted the rest of his life to engineering. While serving as an assistant lecturer in Naval Architecture and Marine Engineering at Glasgow University, he became interested in aeronautics and built a primary monoplane glider that he named the *Bat*. Before it was completed and ready to fly, Pilcher paid a visit to Otto Lilienthal in Germany, received some instruction, and made several glider flights under Lilienthal's guidance.

On returning to Glasgow, Pilcher realized that his *Bat* required considerable modification, after which he made several successful glides from a hill near the banks of the Clyde at Cardross, and by September 1895 had won his place as the first Englishman to complete a true glider flight. Pilcher then seriously considered applying some sort of engine power, but continued with his experiments with gliders. He had varying success and many painful accidents. In 1896 he built two more that he named the *Gull* and the *Hawk;* the latter a great improvement on his previous productions. It had a wingspan of 23 feet, and an area of 180 square feet that gave the *Hawk* a loading of a trifle over one pound per square foot.

The *Hawk* was stabilized by movements of the pilot's body, and when aboard Pilcher performed a series of long glides and learned much about controlling the glider in flight. When he made a flight of 250 yards in June 1897 he decided to design an engine suitable for powered flight. In the meantime he had listened to a lecture given by Lawrence Hargrave on the subject of soaring kites, and he then designed a triplane glider that incorporated many of Hargrave's ideas, but before he could test out his new theories he was fatally injured in a glider accident.

With an engine built into his triplane during that summer of 1899, Pilcher planned to attempt a trial flight at Market Harborough in Leicestershire on September 30, but foggy weather caused a postponement, so he decided to give an exhibition with the *Hawk* instead. After taking off successfully an important guy wire snapped when Pilcher was about 30 feet in the air, the glider collapsed, and the pilot was so seriously injured in the crash he died two days later.

Hiram Maxim's Marvelous Machine

The scientific world was drawn a long step nearer the secret of mechanical flight in 1893 when Sir Hiram Maxim, an American inventor and scientist, turned his mind to the problem. Born in Sangerville, Maine, in 1840, Maxim began his career with an engineering firm in Fitchburg, Massachusetts. Later, he was chief engineer of the United States Electric Lighting Company, the first organization of its kind in America. Meanwhile Maxim became interested in explosives and weapons, and in the course of his work went to Great Britain in 1881. He later became a British subject, and organized the Maxim Gun Company that merged with the

Nordenfeldt Company of Germany in 1888. He was, of course, the inventor of the Maxim machine gun, one of the first reliable automatic weapons of that period, and after the Boer War was knighted by Queen Victoria.

There is no truth in the various reports that Maxim invented his weapon in America, and upon its being ignored by his own government, he had taken it to England where he was warmly welcomed. The fact of the matter is that the gun idea that had been in his mind for some time was brought to some fruition when he was visiting Paris in 1881 as an agent of his American electrical company. After receiving the French Legion of Honor for his contribution to electrical science, he was advised by another American he met in Vienna to forget chemistry and electricity: "If you wish to make a pile of money invent something that will enable these Europeans to cut each other's throats with greater facility."

And with that, so Maxim stated later in a letter, he remembered making a set of drawings for a hand-worked machine gun, and improved on this and turned out a fully automatic rifle. In the course of events he showed the new drawings to a Scotsman he had known in Paris and New York. The Scotsman invited Maxim to come to London where the American set up a small workshop at 57d Hatton Garden. Here the Maxim gun was turned out, perfected and patented. By 1885 British government trials were arranged, and contracts drawn for the manufacture of the gun by Messrs. Vickers, then located at Crayford in Kent.

Other nations showed keen interest in the weapon and Hiram Maxim was soon a very rich man. With his fertile mind he naturally turned to new fields.

Aerial navigation, as it was being developed by Clement Ader and Otto Lilienthal, won Maxim's interest, and in a few years he had spent around $200,000 in the development of a huge steam-powered "multiplane" that weighed 3½ tons. This machine was twenty-five times the size of any of the gliders of the day, and bore enormous monoplane wings of 5550 square feet. In addition to this great central plane, it carried five hinged planes on either side that were to provide control for equilibrium, as well as large front and rear rudders. Its twin propellers were 17-feet, 10-inches long, and were turned by a 350-horsepower steam engine that burned benzine for fuel. The whole structure was built mainly of steel tubing and silk. The tubing served two purposes; for framework, and a circulation system by which the used steam was condensed to water and used over again.

Maxim's first aim was to prove that such a machine could fly, but he had no intention of piloting it in the air. He mounted this machine on a running gear that weighed more than 3000 pounds, but there was a lighter underbody available, should he prove his first point.

With all this power, the 110-foot-wide wing, and the great propellers, it seemed certain that the Maxim plane would get off the ground. His final test was made in September 1894. The heavy running gear was mounted on a half-mile of railroad track, and Sir Hiram and an assistant climbed aboard. The engine was fired up, the propellers started, the great machine began its journey along the track, and within a few seconds was straining against a dual guard rail intended to restrain it from rising more than six inches. There is no question that it would have flown free, had not its inventor brought it to earth. As it was, it almost ripped the railroad track from its bed, and continued on to plow through a crash barrier at the end of the run.

"Propulsion and lifting problems have been solved,"

Maxim said after the wild test, "the rest is a mere matter of time."

The "mere matter of time," proved to be a few weeks short of ten years. Maxim never attempted to fly his own invention again, but ended his days making very profound statements concerning the theory of flight. He was disliked widely by other experimenters, Wilbur Wright, in particular, who wrote in 1908: "I doubt the goodness of his purposes, and dislike his personality. He is an awful blow, and abuses his brother and son scandalously." Maxim's son, Hiram Percy, was the inventor of the Maxim Silencer for guns, and his brother, Hudson, was an expert in explosives.

The Saga of Santos-Dumont

One of the truly great figures in early twentieth-century aviation was Alberto Santos-Dumont, son of a wealthy Brazilian coffee planter. An active, imaginative youth, Alberto drove locomotives on his father's plantation, and when he was fifteen witnessed a balloon ascension at São Paolo. He had begged to be taken aloft, but his father refused to permit his son to take such a risk. He was kept at home in Brazil until he was eighteen when he was sent to Paris to study motorcar transport. There he made the acquaintance of two French aeronauts, La Chambre and Machuron, who had built a balloon for the Swedish scientist Salomon A. Andrée, who, in 1897, made a gallant, but fatal attempt to reach the North Pole. Alberto who was then twenty-four, paid the two French balloonists 250 francs to take him aloft in a spherical balloon, and in a short time Santos-Dumont coffee money was being funneled into the building of dirigibles.

He first contrived a simple cylindrical balloon of varnished Japanese silk with pointed ends, below which he swung a light basket, and mounted a 3½-horsepower gasoline engine taken from a tricycle to operate a small propeller. Once in the air, Santos-Dumont controlled the angle of ascent or descent by shifting a series of weights, for and aft. The lateral direction was handled by a simple rudder.

His first flight with this contrivance was a classic. Taking off from the Zoological Gardens in Paris on September 20, 1898, he rose majestically, and sailed away at an altitude of 1500 feet toward Longchamp. Nothing like this had been seen before by any of the professional aeronauts who had gathered to witness the display. But to descend, Alberto had to release considerable gas, and then discovered that his small engine would not pump in air fast enough to keep the long cylindrical bag extended. In a few minutes the dirigible began to fold in the middle, and the whole machine fell at excessive speed.

Looking below, he spotted several boys flying kites at Bagatelle, and giving them a new hobby, he yelled down, "Catch my guide rope and run against the wind!" The kite fliers worked manfully, and obeyed Santos-Dumont's instructions so well his collapsing balloon acted like a kite and landed safely on the turf.

A year later the young South American had built his second dirigible, and a third was completed and flown in November 1899. Santos-Dumont was so entranced with the success of his dirigibles, he built a factory at Saint-Cloud, and in 1901 put on a show with his fifth airship that startled the world.

This flight was made when M. Deutsch de la Meurthe, noted French sportsman, offered a prize of 125,000 francs to any airman who would fly around the Eiffel Tower

within a designated time of thirty minutes. Although he had
no need of the money, Santos-Dumont was determined to
make the attempt, and actually incurred a serious risk in
taking off when he did. Those who witnessed the flight were
astonished to see the frail-looking machine take off, head
across the Auteil racecourse and along the Bois de Boulogne,
bucking and bouncing against a stiff wind. But the spectators were speechless when they saw him guide the ungainly
balloon around the tall structure, so close the diners in the
upper restaurant could look down on the South American
as he held the controls in the small wicker basket. Clearing the tower and the tempestuous winds, Santos-Dumont
headed back for Saint-Cloud, passing over the heads of the
timekeepers in just 29½ minutes from his starting time. He
had won the prize by 30 seconds!

The 125,000 francs (about $15,000 then) he divided be-
tween his employees and the Paris poor. The Paris Aero
Club had donated an additional "Encouragement" prize of
4000 francs which Alberto returned to the club to set up
another aviation prize. The Brazilian government awarded
him a gold medal and 125,000 francs.

This was Alberto's third attempt to circle the Eiffel
Tower. In the first he landed in a chestnut tree near the
château of Princess Isabel, daughter of Dom Pedro of
Brazil. Hearing of the mishap, the Princess sent him a breakfast in a lunch basket and invited him to call on her. A day
or two later she sent him a medal of St. Benedict "that
protects against all accidents." He wore it on a gold chain
around his wrist, and from that day on came through unscathed, although some of his flights were hair-raising. For
instance, on his second attempt to fly around the Eiffel
Tower, his Number 5 airship was destroyed by an explosion
after he had had to land on the roof of the Hotel Trocadero.

In the years that followed, till the outbreak of World War I, Santos-Dumont built fourteen dirigibles, all of which he put at the command of the French government in case of war against any other power, "except Brazil and the United States."

This South American's role in aviation was not confined to lighter-than-air dirigibles, though his work in that field was recognized by scientists of all nations; in 1899 Professor Samuel P. Langley made a special trip from America to France to watch Santos-Dumont's exhibitions and to learn some of his findings. But in 1906, Santos-Dumont made the first aeroplane flight in Europe, an accomplishment to be presented in a later chapter.

Lanchester and Prandtl

While many aeronauts were risking life and limb—to say nothing of their personal finances—to further the cause of heavier-than-air flight, there were others who were making contributions in a less dramatic manner. They were the stolid thinkers, scientists who could analyze what the aeronauts were doing, point out the mistakes, and put their findings down on paper in the form of charts, graphs, and written rules. These were the slipstick boys of the early aerial age, and their contributions perhaps were even more vital than the hair-raising glider and balloon exhibitions.

One of these men, Frederick W. Lanchester, a noted British engineer who was born in 1868, began early to make a study of mechanical flight and before 1900 had produced a model that was stable in a high wind. In 1884 Lanchester read before a Birmingham scientific society a paper titled

The Theory of Flight, and by 1908 had produced two volumes on aerodynamics and aerodonetics, in which two works and in an earlier paper he introduced his now famous hypothesis of flight based on the vortex theory. This view was ignored by most scientists in his own country, but it was developed brilliantly by Ludwig Prandtl, the German scientist, and several others.

Although Lanchester was ignored for years by his own country, it was soon realized elsewhere that this Englishman had one of the keenest minds on aeronautics. In 1914 Lanchester produced a book, *Aircraft Warfare,* in which he introduced the N Square Law and its application to fighting tactics. That same year he read the James Forrest lecture before the International Engineering Congress at San Francisco, and in 1926 he read the Wilbur Wright Memorial lecture before the Royal Aeronautical Society and was awarded the society's gold medal.

Ludwig Prandtl also contributed a great deal to the science. Trained as an engineer, this Bavarian was on the staff of the Hanover Technical High School where he began the study of air through pipes. In 1904 he was appointed professor at the University of Göttingen, and there studied the flow of gases. While thus engaged Prandtl was consulted by Die Motor-Luftschiff-Studiengesellschaft of Berlin, a firm assigned to produce the *Parseval* airship, which was designed to carry three-man crews, and actually intended for sporting events or flying clubs. Prandtl suggested building a wind tunnel that was completed in 1908, and two years later the German professor made a serious study of aeroplane wings mounted in this wind tunnel and by 1913 furnished reliable calculations on induced resistance. He next made a study of eddy formations behind bodies, and completed a development of the Lanchester theory. He, too, was awarded the Gold Medal of the Royal Aeronautical Society.

Samuel Pierpont Langley began his scientific life as an astronomer, and it was while he was professor of physics and astronomy at the Allegheny Observatory of Western University of Pennsylvania, now the University of Pittsburgh, that he first became known for his remarkable mind (he had only a high school education) and ability to cope with difficult problems. He invented a bolometer to determine the distribution of heat in the spectrum of the sun. When he was appointed Secretary of the Smithsonian Institution in November 1887, Langley took up the problems of heavier-than-air flight, and from that point on his powered models attracted the attention of all American scientists.

James Glaisher, another British scientist, contributed much to the aeronautical world, not only by his balloon ascensions, but because he applied his knowledge of meteorology to the varied problems encountered. In fact, Glaisher was the first man to put meteorology on a scientific basis. As early as 1862 he made three ascents, and his scientific observations were printed in the British Meteorological Society's reports for that year. That same year—1862— Glaisher accompanied Henry Coxwell in a remarkable ascent when their balloon reached a height of 37,000 feet, at which time both men lost consciousness, but fortunately Coxwell recovered sufficiently to pull the release valve cord with his teeth, thus starting the balloon back to earth. In subsequent ascents Glaisher reached heights of 10,000 to 20,000 feet, always searching for new secrets to be found in the clouds.

The Contribution of Chanute

Born in Paris in 1832 but brought to the United States when he was six years old, Octave Chanute probably contributed more to the inspiration of the Wright brothers than any man in the aeronautical world. Chanute was not only a theorist, but he made more than seven hundred glider flights without an accident. All this provided valuable basic knowledge, and fortunately he put his findings, tables, and opinions on paper.

As a young man Octave Chanute worked as a railroad bridge engineer, and by 1872 had risen to the post of chief engineer of the Erie Railroad, and later held positions with several western lines. He also designed the Union Stock Yards for both Chicago and Kansas City.

Little was known in America of the glider until, after much reading and experimentation, Chanute produced a simple biplane in 1896, using truss construction he had learned in bridge building. From the beginning, the glider's stability in flight, efficiency, and ease of handling far outstripped anything previously produced. Chanute, who was now well over sixty, was assisted in this work by Augustus M. Herring and William Avery who worked with him in a laboratory they had built in Chicago. Most of their early glides were made from the sand dunes along Lake Michigan some thirty miles east of Chicago. In June 1896 they built a flying camp there, and were joined later by William P. Butusov who built and flew Le Bris-type gliders, and a Dr. Ricketts who willingly acted as cook, just to be in on the venture. They experimented there for two summers and even built a Lilienthal model that they tried out.

Chanute and his assistants soon discovered that the Lilienthal and Pilcher models required exhaustive shifting of weight to retain stability, a point that confirmed Chanute's theory that inherent stability was imperative to safe flight. In other words, the operator was well-occupied in steering the contrivance without going through strenuous contortions to keep it in level flight.

In the beginning Chanute concentrated on a 12-plane glider, but this required too much accurate rigging for simple efficiency, so he kept reducing the number of planes until he had them down to five. Even this arrangement was inefficient, so he finally settled for a simple biplane, offering 135 square feet of wing area, weighing only 23 pounds, and which would carry a 160–180-pound man at 20 to 40 miles per hour. Actually, more than 2000 glides were made by various forms of the Chanute glider, no less than seven hundred of them by Chanute himself.

In 1898 Augustus Herring, Octave's chief assistant, was convinced that their biplane glider was ready for power, but Chanute argued that further experiments in automatic stability were first needed. So Herring went to work on his own and built a Chanute-type biplane with a double tail, and mounted a compressed-air engine. He appears to have settled on a three-foot-long compressed-air tank that was applied to two two-bladed propellers, mounted fore and aft. After some experiments, Herring insisted he had made a flight of a few seconds, but his claim was never verified or accepted.

Before his aeronautical life was finished, Chanute produced his great work, *Progress in Flying Machines*, that was read avidly by the Wright brothers before they started their experiments. Chanute, too, was awarded the Gold Medal of the Royal Aeronautical Society in 1910.

The Trials of Mr. Montgomery

This chapter cannot be closed without a formal introduction to Professor John J. Montgomery of Santa Clara, California, another American scientist who played a controversial role in the development of heavier-than-air flying. He is said by some to have been the first American to construct and maneuver gliders successfully; by others to have been a misguided experimenter who often made boastful claims without producing reliable evidence of his achievements. In fact, many of his assertions were not made until 1905—two years after the Wrights had flown at Kitty Hawk —but apparently much of the fault may be charged to Professor Montgomery's reticence while developing his several types.

The Santa Clara inventor first began his experiments around 1883–86 when he built three machines, based on the flapping-wing design, but like Hargrave, he had little success beyond the development of very small models. Around 1885 he made a glider with wings that were planned on those of the gull. His craft had a wingspread of 20 feet, and the wings were 4½ feet in depth, indicating that the Californian had come close to the most suitable aspect ratio for a glider. Aspect ratio is the proportion of the chord, or depth, of a wing to its length.

From the accounts which were sparse in those days, success was attained almost immediately, and on one occasion a glide of 600 feet was attained. But greater efforts were hindered by lack of equilibrium, and Montgomery went back to his drawing board, and also put in many hours watching vultures in flight. In 1885 he constructed another glider, and though the principle of equilibrium used in a bird's wing was followed, the form of its section was ignored, because it seemed unreasonable to Montgomery that any wing should be curved downward at the front. This machine was fitted with wings with flat surfaces and to provide lateral stability each wing was hinged diagonally. This diagonal hinge permitted the "flaps" thus formed to yield to undue pressure on either side. They were held in their normal position by light springs. Thus, if the pressure became excessive the flap of that wing would yield proportionately.

In addition to the hinge-spring arrangement, a saddle seat was mounted on an upright to which were attached wires that ran to the rear portion of the wings. When the operator leaned to one side or the other he automatically depressed or raised the camber of the wing, but this movement did not set up varied angles of incidence, as the Wright's wing-warping design did later. The shifting of weight in Montgomery's design was used to "improve" stability, not just to set up a banking attitude in turns. In flight Montgomery's glider provided excellent control, but its gliding efficiency was very low, so the professor worked out a third version.

Again, the Californian was long on aeronautical control, but short on the ability to design a glider that would give flights of length or duration. He experimented with half a dozen models, but it was not until he learned the reason for the forward curve of a bird's wing that he finally attained success. He came upon this secret while watching light thistledown blown toward a barn door set at an angle of 10 degrees, and he was astonished to note that the movement of the down showed clearly that the wind, instead of moving in a straight line at the leading edge of the barn door, traveled in a gradual curve and rose to strike the surface, indicating that the surface had an action on the wind in front of it, and making plain the reason for the curving surface of a bird's wing. This is an oversimplified explanation of air flow over a cambered airfoil, but sufficient to explain the phenomenon.

By 1903 Professor Montgomery had a wealth of information in hand and was aware of the fundamental principles of flight. He was ready to put them into practice and was making astounding displays by 1905–06. It may seem strange, this continued glider experimentation so long after the Wrights had shown the world how to fly a powered machine, but it must be recalled that few people knew that powered flight had been accomplished, and when the fact was mentioned not many believed it. As a result many experimenters—including the Wrights—continued to test out their theories with gliders.

Montgomery was thrilling the West Coast with his displays, and his gliders usually were piloted by Daniel Maloney, a daring parachute jumper of that time. Starting with lifts up to a thousand feet, Maloney made free-flight exhibitions that amazed the crowds below. Later on, he ascended to 4000 feet in a Montgomery glider that weighed only 45 pounds, and again held the watchers spellbound with his complex maneuvers as he returned to earth. His repertoire included sharp turns, spirals, figure eights, hairraising dives, and other astonishing evolutions with rare skill and grace. On one occasion Maloney flew a distance of eight miles in the space of twenty minutes, and landed lightly on his feet at a designated field.

This daring young man was killed in 1905 as the result of an accident that was argued and discussed for years, in and out of court. According to Montgomery's version; in

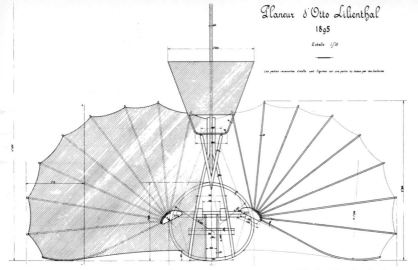

"To fly is everything," proclaimed Otto Lilienthal, German scientist, who st established the principles of bird flight in human gliding. Here is a awing of his 1895 glider with which he made flights of between 100 rds and a quarter of a mile. The glider is on view at the National Museum Washington.

Octave Chanute, American civil engineer, improved on the Lilienthal der and concentrated on developing inherent stability. With this biplane der Chanute and his assistant Augustus M. Herring made more than a ousand successful flights without accident.

3. In 1902 the Wright brothers designed a glider incorporating wing-war[ing lateral control, and with this solved the secret of controlled flight. He[re] Wilbur is seen gliding at Kitty Hawk. True powered flight was only o[ne] year away.

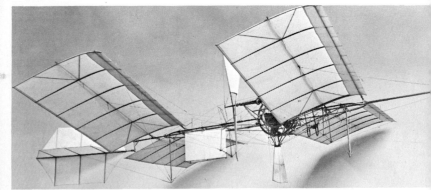

4. The ¼ size model of Professor Langley's "Aerodrome" which in 189[6] flew a distance of 4200 feet over the Potomac River. The model was pow[ered with a 1½ horsepower steam engine. On the strength of this succe[ss] President McKinley induced the Board of Ordnance to appropriate $50,00[0] to build a full-scale machine. The man-carrying version was a total failur[e]

Professor Samuel P. Langley's famed "Aerodrome" machine mounted for
ht on a catapult launching gear set up on a houseboat. Two attempts were
de to fly off, but both ended in failure. The "Aerodrome" was powered
h a radial engine designed by Charles M. Manly.

n 1868 John Springfellow, British engineer, built this steam-powered,
ane model which flew a short distance at London's Crystal Palace. To-
's experts believe that had a suitable engine been available, a full-scale
hine would have flown, carrying a pilot. This model is still on view at
National Museum in Washington.

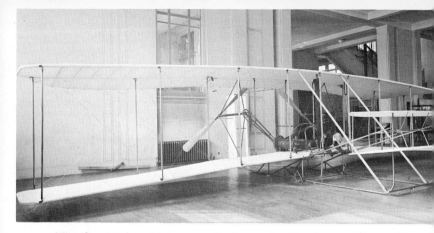

7. The first Wright biplane on display at the Kensington Science Museum in London after it had been rebuilt. The original machine was badly damaged at Kitty Hawk after its last flight, and then packed up and returned to Dayton. Some months later the dismantled flier was further damaged after a flash flood inundated the city but as much as could be salvaged was incorporated into the rebuilding job. The machine is now on display at the Smithsonian Institution in Washington.

U.S. Air Force Photo

8. The Wright biplane designed for the first military trial at Fort Myer, Virginia, during the summer of 1908. It was aboard this machine that Lieutenant Thomas E. Selfridge was fatally injured while flying as an official observer. Orville Wright, the pilot, was badly hurt but recovered.

being lifted by a hot-air balloon Maloney's glider was damaged by one of the guy ropes used to control the early ascent. Officials on the ground shouted to him, warning him not to cut loose, but the parachute jumper apparently did not hear their cries. He pulled his release at a height of 4000 feet, and the machine suddenly turned over and began to drop upside down. Oddly enough, Maloney did not appear to fall much faster than he would have done had he been making a parachute descent, and when the wrecked glider was reached Maloney was found to have no broken bones or serious body injury, but he was unconscious and died thirty minutes later. Attending physicians concluded that he had died of heart failure.

From that time on all of Montgomery's flights and claims were criticized by certain groups of the aeronautical world. The Wrights, for instance, were positive that the Californian's designs were not following the correct principle of flight, and that the Maloney tragedy did not happen as reported.

All of Montgomery's 1905–06 flights, however, appear to have been attested by newspaper reports and articles written by responsible science writers of the time. The *Scientific American* of May 20, 1905, stated, "An aeroplane has been constructed that in all circumstances will retain its equilibrium and is subject in its gliding flight to the control and guidance of an operator." According to Victor Loughead, an aeronautical expert and writer on automotive and engineering subjects, Octave Chanute characterized the first Maloney flight as the "most daring feat ever attempted," and Alexander Graham Bell had no hesitation in asserting that "all subsequent attempts in aviation must begin with the Montgomery machine."

All this poured fuel on the bitter controversy that was

raging over several factors in the progress of mechanical flight. The Wrights derided Montgomery's efforts for years, and argued that he was employing a dangerous design and they could have predicted that one day Maloney would be killed. They put no stock in the balloon guy-rope entanglement, though it probably was true, but insisted that Montgomery's persistence in placing cambered wings in tandem was risking tragic results. In fact, Montgomery himself was killed in October 1911 at Evergreen, California, while gliding in one such machine.

This bitterness was hashed and rehashed years later when Loughead induced the Montgomery family to sue the United States government for infringement on his combination of curved surfaces "with warping wings." The Court of Claims decided against the Montgomery heirs, explaining that "It seems to us idle to contend that Montgomery was a pioneer in this particular art."

CHAPTER III

On the Theshold

A Day of Destiny • The Saga of the Wrights • On to Kitty Hawk • The Wright Engine • Assisted Take-off • No Prophets in Their Own Land

The opening of the twentieth century saw man on the threshold of the greatest creative evolution in history. The automobile, powered with a satisfactory internal combustion engine, was an accepted vehicle, and the civilized world was having to readjust to this new mode of transportation. John Holland had devised a submarine that proved its worth after several false starts, and had been accepted by the United States Navy. The Paris Exposition opened with its aeronautical exhibition. Guglielmo Marconi tapped out the first wireless message to cross the Atlantic from England to Newfoundland, and the First International Arbitration Court was convened at The Hague. Count von Zeppelin of Germany made his first successful dirigible flight over Lake Constance, establishing a navigation-by-airship era that was to hold the world's attention for more than thirty years. But in the field of mechanical flight the pendulum of destiny swung between the American rivals, Professor Langley and the Wright brothers.

We turn first to Professor Samuel P. Langley's effort, the climax of a long fruitful scientific career. He began his work in aeronautics with a rather cursory inquiry into the accepted principles of powered flight, following which he questioned the soundness of the prevailing ideas of how birds fly. He devised a whirling table on which he tested out several theories, and concluded that it was possible to construct "machines that would give such veolcity to inclined surfaces that bodies definitely heavier than air could be sustained upon it and moved through it with great speed." After making a study of the irregularities of the winds, he went on with the construction of several flying models.

During May 1896 Professor Langley built a machine he called an *Aerodrome,* a device weighting 26 pounds that was 16 feet in length and had a wingspan of 13 feet. In trial flights this machine twice sustained itself in the air for about one and one-half minutes, or for the full endurance of its steam engine's fuel and water. On each of these occasions Langley's *Aerodrome* flew a distance of well over half a mile and than landed gently on the surface of the Potomac River over which it had been launched. Later in that same year another model of this type flew a distance of three-quarters of a mile, attaining a speed of 30 miles per hour. The scientific world had never seen anything comparable to this, and it was believed generally that Professor Langley was well on the way to successful mechanical flight.

Shortly after the close of the Spanish-American War, President William McKinley, who had been concerned that the Germans were considering the possibility of using

Count Zeppelin's airships as weapons of war, made some inquiries and learned that Langley, then head of the Smithsonian Institution, had been experimenting with models of powered aircraft. When he was informed that the professor had concluded his aeronautical quest, satisfied that powered flight was possible, President McKinley persuaded the War Department to appropriate $50,000 for advanced work, and this sum was turned over to Professor Langley.

As secretary of the leading scientific institution in the country, Langley had a number of fine minds at his command, among them a young mechanical engineer, Charles M. Manly who had built what may be accepted as the forerunner of the American radial engine, a 5-cylindered power plant arranged around a master crankshaft. This idea was not completely original with Manly, for variations of the type had been under development for a number of years. The fan, or star, arrangement of cylinders had been designed to cut down the over-all weight of the engine, a feature that had marked the efforts of the Anzani firm in France, the M.A.B. company in Italy, and the Farcot concern in France which had produced an air-cooled, 6-cylinder power plant.

A man by the name of Forest probably had originated the idea in 1888, but Manly was among the first to use it as an aviation engine. Forest had first built an 8-cylinder, 50-horsepower engine of this type, and later designed one that produced one horsepower for each eleven pounds of engine weight. Langley previously had contracted for a 12-horsepower engine of this type that would not weigh more than a hundred pounds, but the manufacturer could not deliver such a power plant. Manly then rose to the occasion with a radial engine that weighed 125 pounds and put out 50 horsepower at 950 revolutions per minute. It developed this full power for ten hours under constant loads and was adapted subsequently for a full-sized version of Langley's *Aerodrome.*

With governmental assistance, plus the enthusiastic support of the Smithsonian Institution and the Aero Club of America, the leading civilian aviation organization Langley had no trouble completing his full-scale *Aerodrome* that was to be launched from a very intricate catapult gear built on top of a Potomac River houseboat. Weeks of careful effort by first-class workmen were expended in modifying the houseboat, the launching device, and the new man-carrying *Aerodrome* that was to be piloted by Manly.

How this young mechanical engineer was expected to accomplish this has always been a puzzle, as no one anywhere had yet flown a powered aircraft, and as far as is known Manly had never had any experience with a simple man-carrying glider. But he was selected by Langley, and to Manly's credit, he willingly undertook the assignment.

A Day of Destiny

Langley's invention was prepared for its initial flight on October 7, 1903, before an impressive group of military and scientific officials. In full-scale form it looked much like an early type monoplane except that it had two broad wings set in tandem at the front and rear of the body framework. Manly's engine was mounted near the center of the fuselage and was geared to drive two pusher propellers through a simple chain-gear system.

The *Aerodrome* was drawn back as far as it would go on the track and Manly climbed aboard, carrying a life jacket over one arm. He wore light-colored trousers, spotless canvas shoes, and had a pair of automobile goggles shoved up on his forehead. Nearby puffed two tugs, provided by the Smithsonian Institution, to carry newspapermen and photographers who were on hand to record the results of more than four years of hard labor.

They saw Manly take his seat, adjust his goggles and start the engine. The gleaming radial went through a slow warm-up, then the pilot eased the throttle up and the two propellers screamed their power. Manly raised his arm as a signal, a workman with an ax cleaved the retaining cable, and the catapult trolley shot forward. The great winged bird surged ahead as the spectators held their breaths in anticipation, but one and all choked on low cries when they saw that the *Aerodrome* was not flying off free and clear. Instead, it was nosing down to the water.

The frightened crowd saw the Langley flying machine, its engine running smoothly and the propellers whirling in unison, hit the water and disappear. The spectators were shocked for a long instant, but cheered when the *Aerodrome* rose from the depths and floated on top of the river. Manly was uninjured and was soon rescued from the wreckage.

Major M. M. Macomb of the United States Artillery who represented the War Department reported in an ambiguous statement: "The trial was unsuccessful because the front guy post caught in its support on the launching car and was not released in time to give free flight, as was intended, but on the contrary caused the machine to plunge into the water about fifty yards in front of the houseboat. The engine was uninjured and the frame only slightly damaged, but the four wings and rudder were practically destroyed by the first plunge and the subsequent towing back to the houseboat. The accident necessitated the re-

moval of the houseboat to Washington for the more convenient repair of the damages."

Although deeply disappointed, Langley and his fellow
scientists were more confident than ever that they had established the true principles of aerodynamics—barring
minor accidents—and that they would enjoy complete success with a second test. Back in Washington the machine
and the catapult gear were completely repaired, and by
December 8, two months after its first trial, the *Aerodrome*
was back on its rack and poised for another trial.

The houseboat was towed back across the Potomac and
anchored off Anacostia not far from the site of the present
day Air Force and Navy flying fields. This time a General
Rudolph accompanied Major Macomb aboard the *Bar-
tholdi* which stood off nearby. Many photographers and
newspapermen were also on hand. The weather was clear,
but raw and gusty with little warmth in the December sun.
Nevertheless, everyone aboard the houseboat was confident
that this time Manly would get away successfully. No one
questioned what he would do if he found himself free and
skimming through the air. All effort thus far had been put
into developing a machine with power that would fly; there
had been little time or thought given to training a man in
handling such a machine in the air.

And so, a second day of destiny saw Langley and Manly
grouped around the *Aerodrome* with their aides, considering the harsh wind, and watching the sun go down. It was
4:45 P.M. when Manly climbed aboard and started the
radial engine. He stiffened in his seat, eased the throttle up,
and the two propellers twirled smoothly. Again, the retaining cable was cut and the catapult car glided forward.
There was an instant when everything seemed to be going
smoothly. The great winged machine gained headway, and

its forward planes seemed to rise at the prescribed angle. Then when success looked certain, when the *Aerodrome* seemed to be leaving the catapult cradle, there was a grinding, rending crash. Langley's machine had actually raised itself off the catapult, but with that effort both rear wings crumpled and the whole tail section collapsed.

For a few seconds the damaged plane struggled with its nose to the sky, the screeching engine striving to drive the front wings and body into the air. Then gravity triumphed and the machine dropped backward into the river before the houseboat that had been unanchored for this test and was moving forward on its own inertia.

Manly went under the water with the machine, and for a time was trapped below when his life preserver became entangled with the wreckage, but he tore the jacket in two and struggled to the surface in the path of the oncoming houseboat and floating ice. A standby crew in a rowboat rescued him, and a tug took over the wreckage of the *Aerodrome*.

The details of this flight were to be discussed and argued hotly for more than a quarter of a century, but Major Macomb's report stated clearly, "The fact remains that the rear wings and rudder were wrecked before the machine was free of the ways."

Many admirers of Professor Langley, however, insisted that his *Aerodrome* had proved itself "capable of flight," and three years later while on his deathbed officials of the Aero Club of America gave him some recognition by proclaiming that he had indeed built the "first successful aeroplane," a statement that was contended heatedly for years.

This controversy reached its highest point in 1914 when friends of the late Professor Langley formed a new scientific group know as the Langley Laboratory and attempted to prove that the scientist's machine was capable of flight. They gathered up the remains of Langley's old *Aerodrome*, reassembled it—supplying many new parts and a more reliable engine. The machine was set up at Hammondsport, New York, and prepared for a demonstration flight.

Griffith Brewer, a noted British aeronaut and close friend of the Wrights, was on hand when the reassembled *Aerodrome* was being prepared, and he reported later in a letter to the New York *Times* that "Glenn Curtiss and Albert F. Zahm, a student of aeronautics, were fitting the old Langley machine with floats, and just as one alteration leads to another, it was found necessary, not to make one or two changes, but in the end to make more than thirty in the structure."

It was explained that many of these changes were dictated by the advanced aeronautical knowledge of 1914. For instance, by this time the Langley Laboratory experts knew that the professor had mistaken the position of the center of pressure and that fault alone would have caused the wings to collapse, so the position of the staying used to support the wings was moved back about three feet. It also was known that the deep camber of the *Aerodrome's* wings was less efficient than the smaller camber of 1914, consequently the wings were changed from a camber of one in 12 to a camber of one in 18. This reduced the area of the wings by 52 square feet.

A final trial was made at Hammondsport on June 2, 1914, with Glenn Curtiss at the controls. This time, under these take-off conditions and the structural modifications, the Langley machine took to the air. "Only a series of short hops of less than five seconds," according to members of the Wright group, but apparently sufficient to satisfy the faith and loyalty of Professor Langley's friends. But it was an effort that only added to the long-standing controversy.

According to Fred C. Kelly, official biographer of the Wrights, Glenn Curtiss had made this attempt simply to prove that a machine that could fly had been built before the Wrights' which in turn would prove that their claims to all aileron controls were not legal. It was the infringement of the Wright lateral control patents that brought about the Wright-Curtiss litigation.

The Saga of the Wrights

Conquest of the air had not as yet been truly won. It was the Wright brothers, two bicycle builders of Dayton, Ohio, who conceived and flew the world's first successful aeroplane. This practical achievement crowned the efforts of thousands of courageous and far-visioned men over more than fifty centuries. These two men accomplished the hitherto impossible on Kill Devil Hill at Kitty Hawk, North Carolina, with a frail contraption, powered with a modified automobile engine. The whole machine had cost less than a thousand dollars.

But their victory in no way detracts from the valuable contributions made by the scientists and inventors who preceded them. The Wrights, however, were unquestionably the first to achieve human flight in a power-driven, heavier-than-air machine 413 years after Leonardo da Vinci sketched his design for a flying machine. This honor has been awarded the Wrights by all nations. France erected a monument to these two Americans, and England was the first to display their historic plane in the South Kensington Science Museum. It is regrettable that their own country did not formally award them their justly won honors until six years after their first memorable flights.

Wilbur Wright was born at Millville, Indiana, in 1867. When he was one month old his father, Milton, moved to Dayton, Ohio, to take on editorial work for the Church of the United Brethren in Christ. Orville was born in Dayton in 1871. There were two older brothers, Reuchlin and Lorin. Their sister Katherine was the baby of the family.

The two older Wright brothers went to college, as did Katherine, but at the end of his high school career Wilbur was injured playing football, and it was decided that he should not go to college. In fact he was something of a semi-invalid for about eight years. Orville who was four years younger was the active member of this duo, whereas Wilbur was the thoughtful one who could write and think things out. Apparently Orville did most of the physical work. Neither brother married.

Their mother, Susan Katherine Koerner, who was born in Virginia of German-American stock, was a hard worker. The boys must have inherited their inventiveness from her, for she was always devising new kitchen utensils, or making one article fit several categories. Once, when money was short, she made a sled for Reuchlin and Lorin. Unfortunately, Mrs. Wright died when Wilbur and Orville were young, and her place was taken by Carrie Grumbach who came into their home as a cook and stayed on until both brothers had died. Their sister Katherine was their especial pal, even when she had gone on to Oberlin College. She helped them build the first biplane that flew by stitching on her sewing machine the linen that was used on the wings. Years later they took her everywhere to share the honors the world bestowed on them.

In their youth both Wilbur and Orville were usually to

be found outdoors, or making things in their little home workshop. At one time they built a printing press from scrap parts and a flat bed made from a discarded tombstone. They printed a four-page weekly newspaper, known as the *West Side Evening Item,* a project that kept them busy for four months. After that they turned to repairing bicycles.

Around 1890 they were involved in the publication of a weekly magazine known as *Snapshots;* mainly to use the facilities of a job printing press they had acquired. This satirical journal was fairly prosperous, but they remained more intrigued with the bicycle business.

In the midst of this activity they decided to manufacture a bicycle of their own design, and, borrowing a small sum of money from the estate of their father's grandmother, Catherine Van Cleve, they went into business and called their machine the Van Cleve Cycle. It was a very good bicycle and the two Dayton young men soon had a sizable bank account.

In 1896 milk was not being pasteurized, and Orville was stricken with typhoid fever, and while convalescing learned of the death of Otto Lilienthal who was killed in a glider accident that year. Wilbur who used to read aloud to his brother wondered what the German scientist had done wrong. "It says he fell off in a sideslip, from which he didn't recover."

"But didn't he have some sort of control to prevent that?" Orville inquired.

"I should think he would have sensed such a slip in time to recover," Wilbur mused.

"If I ever try gliding my machine would be built so that it would have some form of natural stability, and set up natural reactions to recover by itself," Orville added.

"It would be fun to try gliding sometime," Wilbur went on. "I wish we knew more about it. Maybe we could find out where Herr Lilienthal had been wrong." He then remembered a book in their sitting room titled *Animal Mechanism*, written by a French scientist, Etienne Jules Marey, which gave structural details on bird flight. They had read this repeatedly, but Wilbur brought it upstairs and read it over again. Before Orville was up and about they had made plans for gliding experiments on their own.

Although they had an intense interest in the prospects of flying, the brothers did not get around to building a glider until 1899 when they produced one that was based on their own principles and theories. They had digested *Animal Mechanism* completely and next searched for more books and printed information. There was little in or around Dayton, so they wrote to the Curator of the Smithsonian Institution, and among the five or six books suggested by the Washington experts was Octave Chanute's *Progress in Flying Machines*, which headed the list.

From that time on most of the profits from the bicycle shop were channeled into an aeronautical library. Many contradictory theories and conflicting data were presented in these books, and the Wrights had gradually to discount or discard much that had been written, and in many cases had to revise the tables and structural mathematics. Much of this came about after they had made some primary experiments outdoors with a five-foot kite with which they tested wind control and the functions of a tail. When they decided to build a real glider, they figured they would need an area where they could work with a wind that blew at 18 miles an hour or more. This time they consulted the United States Weather Bureau in Washington and learned that there were many places along the Atlantic coast where steady winds of between 16 and 25 miles an hour could be experienced. Then the Weather Bureau observer at Kitty Hawk, North Carolina, told them of nearby sand dunes and low hills from which they might make glider experiments. With all this information at hand, the Wrights decided to visit Kitty Hawk during the summer of 1900.

On to Kitty Hawk

Kitty Hawk was found to be a small fishing village on the narrow sand strip between Albemarle Sound and the Atlantic Ocean. There was one special stretch of sandy area, one mile wide, and about five miles long, with one bare hill about eighty feet high in its center. There was not a tree or bush to be seen, and the winds usually were from the north and northeast during September and October. Elizabeth City, North Carolina, was twenty-five miles away by boat that brought supplies and mail three days a week. There was no hotel or boardinghouse and the Wrights had to plan to house themselves in a tent and take meals with a private family. They finally built a square shed that was used as a hangar, workshop, and a quick-snack kitchen. Lumber and materials were obtained at the J. E. Ethridge Company's mill in Norfolk. All their supplies had to be hauled to Elizabeth City and put aboard the boat for Kitty Hawk. A bill for some light pine for main spars that came to $2.70 is still among the Wright documents.

After some agonizing experiences getting from the mainland to Kitty Hawk, the two Dayton men finally went to work. At this point their history is somewhat vague concerning whether they built their first glider in Dayton and shipped it to Kitty Hawk, or bought lumber for main spars in Norfolk, and added the ribs, linen and other items that were made at home, when they had settled on the sand dunes. Apparently a great deal of their time was given to building the shed, one side of which was hinged so that it could be raised to furnish shade when the hangar was in use. At any rate, their first glider was a simple biplane affair with wings 18 feet wide and 5 feet deep. It had no tail, as such, but carried a novel front "elevator" that was rigged to give horizontal control and prevent nose dives. This feature was original with the Wrights.

At first this glider was flown as a kite with cables looping down to an operator on the ground, and rigged in such a manner that he could raise or lower the nose elevator and in that way control the horizontal attitude of the machine. Next, they decided it was safe enough to place a pilot aboard, and in this they established a new practice. Instead of standing up inside the framework and running into the wind, the Wrights decided to have the pilot lie prone on the lower wing. Captain William J. Tate of the nearby Coinjock lighthouse, along with one of the brothers, helped to raise and launch the glider and send it sailing down the hill into the prevailing wind.

Their first efforts were not spectacular, but they were certain they were on the right track and that their type of controls was correct. During these flights they pondered on why Otto Lilienthal had been killed, and there was a time when they decided that the German scientist had crashed as the result of the behavior of a faulty tail, and in following this theory through they developed a wing-warping control, a primary variant of the aileron. It was this device that led them into one of the country's bitterest legal suits when they were opposed by another group headed by

Alexander Graham Bell and Glenn Curtiss who argued that the Wrights' wing-warping idea was actually originated by designers Jean-Marie le Bris, D'Esterno, and Louis Mouillard, and that the Wright control was a combination of curved surfaces *with* wing-warping, and as an aside they stated that it was nothing more than a direct infringement on a patent by Professor Montgomery.

During the following winter the Wrights modified some of their first impressions, drew new plans and built a second glider that they took to Kitty Hawk in the late summer of 1901. This model was larger than the first, having a wingspan of 22 feet and a chord of 7 feet. Interestingly enough, the wings of their first glider had a curve (camber) of one in 22, but in the second they took Lilienthal's data and used a curve of one in 12. They discovered that this was wrong, for the center of air pressure under the wing moved too fast and the glider was difficult to control. So they re-rigged the wings and employed a curve of one in 18, and following this change, made a glide of 398 feet with perfect fore and aft control. When they had perfected their wing-warping device they discovered they could glide with comparative safety against a 27-mile-an-hour wind.

What had been a pleasant recreation now became a definite scientific pursuit. They were convinced that most existing aeronautical data were wrong, and dangerous, so to prove their theories they built during the next winter the world's first wind tunnel. Ludwig Prandtl, the German scientist, did not complete his airfoil testing device until 1908.

In 1902 the Wrights built a third glider, their most advanced model so far. It had a 32-foot wingspan and a chord of 5 feet, and was fitted with an advanced version of their wing-warping control and an elevator and rudder. They made more than a thousand flights at Kitty Hawk with this glider, and the pilot—Wilbur or Orville—was in full command of the machine in the air at all times. They were positive that they were now ready to try powered flight.

Although dozens of fine photographs of the Wrights' gliding activities had been taken, and a number of the inhabitants of Kitty Hawk village had seen their flights, there were practically no accounts of the activities in any American newspaper. Octave Chanute visited them and saw many of their efforts, and when he was in Paris later on in that year, he gave a talk before the Aero Club of France concerning the Wrights' experiments and explained some details of their system of control. Almost immediately several French experimenters made use of this information and built gliders of the "Wright type," which several historians have declared marked the beginning of European powered flight.

But as far as American interest was concerned, the two Dayton men might as well have been experimenting in goat husbandry on the Gobi Desert.

Ironically, following their success with the 1902 glider, Wilbur, hoping to improve their finances, wrote to the manager of the Redpath Lyceum Bureau suggesting they book him on a series of talks or lectures in which he would discourse on man's attempts to fly, and perhaps explain the many problems involved.

The bureau manager was not too impressed, but admitted that if enough humor could be introduced, there might be a possibility that the bureau could furnish a slide-projector operator, and they might be able to pay Wilbur fifty or seventy-five dollars for each lecture—*less the bureau's twenty per cent commission.*

The Wright Engine

The year 1903 will remain forever a jewel in the crown of aviation, for it was then the Wright boys decided to apply power to their Number 4, or Model A glider. This machine was a smart-looking biplane, equipped with a forward elevator structure and double tail rudders. Space for an engine had been built on the lower main spars, and twin pusher propellers had been devised and set up on suitable spider supports mounted on rear wing struts. They had everything lined up—except an engine. With little to go by, except what the automobile manufacturers of 1903 were putting in their cars, the Wrights designed their own, and Charles E. Taylor, their bicycle shop machinist, built it in six weeks. According to some accounts, they took a Pope-Toledo automobile engine that delivered about 12 horsepower, and with certain refinements and heavier valve springs, they hoped to raise the output to 16 horsepower. It was a 4-cycle engine with four cylinders that were cast independently of gray iron, while the crank case of unusual depth became the oil tank (a new feature in such engines). This shell was cast of aluminum alloy as were the water jackets of the cylinders. The exhaust valves were mounted in cages opening directly into the air and were operated by means of rocker arms through a cam shaft.

Some critics have stated that the Wright engine was very crude in design and far behind the best automobile practice, but these arguments are unfair. The Wrights were not designing an automobile engine, although they may have made use of automobile engine parts; their question was how to furnish sufficient horsepower, a high rate of revolutions, and a weight factor suitable for their over-all problem. What they accomplished after a winter of experimentation was a 150-pound engine that gave 13 horsepower, which was raised later to 16 horsepower, although they had figured that they could have lifted their plane and pilot load of 625 pounds with 8 or 9 horsepower.

But the Wrights encountered another difficulty that is seldom mentioned in a story of the brothers. Once they had an engine, they looked for information on the design and construction of an air propeller but found little. Volumes had been written on the theory and design of marine propellers, but as far as air propellers were concerned there was considerable conflict of opinion.

They had to learn that each part of an airscrew (propeller) blade has a cross section similiar to that of an airfoil (wing), and that in some cases the same shape of section could be used for both purposes. Thus, the thrust of the propeller is obtained by the fact that the chord at each part of the blade is inclined at a small angle—similiar to the angle of attack of an airfoil—to its direction of motion. The thrust of the propeller corresponds to the lift of the wing, and the drag is represented by the resistance of the air to the rotary motion of the propeller blades.

How much of this theory the Wrights knew or followed is difficult to assess. We do know that they eventually turned out two wooden airscrews that were copied later by many other experimenters in Europe. Their manufacture was simple; several lengths of suitable wood were offset on one another in such a manner that when the superfluous wood represented by their protruding edges was removed, the form thus obtained was the basic curvature desired in the finished propeller. The center, or hub, was properly finished, and toothed sprockets bolted to this central boss. The blades were hand finished, polished, and finally varnished. The propellers used on the original Wright biplane were about eight feet in diameter.

When the Wrights returned to Kitty Hawk in September 1903 they found that their camp and hangar had been wrecked by the heavy storms of the winter before, so some time was spent in putting the place in order. They continued to make important glider tests with their Number 2 machine, but also gave considerable attention to the assembling of their Model A. This required three weeks, and they did not have Taylor's engine mounted and ready to run until late November. Meanwhile, Professor Langley had had his first setback on the Potomac when his *Aerodrome* plunged into the river on October 7. The Wrights knew that every effort would be made to repair the machine and to make a second try, but bad weather hindered operations at Kill Devil Hill, and while running their engine and propellers inside the new shed a cracked propeller shaft developed. Orville had to rush back to Dayton to get Taylor to turn out a new one. He returned on December 11, also bringing the news that Langley had failed for the second time and possibly had given up the venture.

Assisted Take-off

After months of consideration the Wrights had decided to launch their Model A from a 60-foot monorail track of wood, covered with sheet-iron strips. (Their catapult device was not introduced until September 1904 when they continued their experiments on a farm near Dayton.) The carriage on which the sledlike skids of the machine rested consisted of a plank 6-feet long on a small trolley device to which were fitted two small wheels, one in front of the other. These were modified hubs from the wheels of a bicycle.

It is interesting to note that a wheeled-undercarriage gear was not introduced for more than three years after the Wrights had first flown, and it was Santos-Dumont, the first man to fly an aeroplane in Europe, who equipped his historic machine with a set of bicycle wheels. Why this had not occurred to the Dayton young men is a mystery, but the track-launching device they used cost $4.00, compared to the very expensive catapult gear devised by Professor Langley.

By December 14 everything was ready but there was little wind, so the Wrights decided to make their first trial on the hill about a quarter of a mile away. Five of their friends from the Life Saving Station came over to help move the machine and launching track to Kill Devil. The track was fastened down, 150 feet up the hill and the biplane set on it facing what wind there was. Wilbur and Orville tossed a coin to see who would make the first attempt, and Wilbur won. He stretched out flat on the lower wing and started the engine. The wind was a trifle to one side, and the track not exactly straight down the hill, creating some difficulty from the start. However, Wilbur admitted later that the failure was due to his own error in judgment because, as the machine began to rise off the track, he nosed it up too steeply, and probably went into a stall. He managed to level off, but the biplane began to mush in with the lack of flying speed, and before he could get the nose down, the machine touched down, sliding sideways. A few members of the front rudder were broken, but Wilbur was more than satisfied that the Model A would fly, that they had enough power, and that all controls were working perfectly—only his piloting was at fault.

All damages had been repaired by December 17. They were ready to try again and this time it was Orville's turn. The morning was bitter cold with a gusty 27-mile wind blowing, and for a time it seemed unwise to make the second attempt. They finally decided to risk a flight from the level area in front of their camp. After warming their hands over a crude stove, they went outside and prepared the machine for its second trial.

Only a handful of witnesses turned up for this epoch-making event. For the record they were John T. Daniels, W. S. Dough, and A. D. Etheridge, friends from the life-saving station. In addition W. C. Brinkley had walked over from Manteo to view the proceedings, and young Johnny Moore, a schoolboy from Nags Head, was also a spectator. One wonders if Johnny realized what a historic event he was to witness.

Orville took his place on the lower wing at 10:30 A.M., started the engine, and ran it for a warmup. The Wright biplane snapped into the teeth of the near gale, rose slowly, and Wilbur was able to run along beside it for about 40 feet. The plane was about four feet in the air by the time it had reached the end of the track, but, under full control, Orville continued on, staying in the air for twelve seconds, covering 120 feet at a speed of 31 miles per hour. Their homemade engine had lifted about 63 pounds per horsepower.

This first flight was recorded by a camera set up by Wilbur who had instructed John Daniels how to trip the shutter when the aircraft had reached a certain point. During the day two very good pictures were obtained in this manner.

Orville said later that on take-off he found the front rudder quite difficult because of its being balanced too near the center; it had a tendency to turn itself when started, and as a result the machine would rise suddenly to a height of about ten feet and then as suddenly, on turning the rudder, it would dart toward the ground. It was one of these sudden dives when it was about a hundred feet beyond the end of the launching track that ended its first flight. Orville's reference to the rudder means, of course, what today would be called the elevator. On the first Wright biplane it was called the front rudder.

At the conclusion of this first flight, it was discovered that the flight lever for controlling the engine was broken, and the skid under the front rudder was cracked. Repairs were made within twenty minutes, and when the machine was brought back to the starting point, Wilbur climbed aboard, anxious to make his second try. He, too, had difficulty with the "rudder" control, but managed to stay in the air for 195 feet.

In a third flight, made shortly before noon, Orville encountered a strong gust from his left that turned the machine off to the right. He immediately applied the elevator-rudder, and then put on some wing-warping control. This worked so well that on landing, the left wing touched down first. In this flight of fifteen seconds, covering 205 feet, Orville had flown at a height of 12 to 14 feet.

At 12:20 P.M. Wilbur started on the fourth and final flight of the day. The biplane again displayed the same sharp up and down movements, but by the time the pilot was out about 400 feet, he had it well under control, and was flying on a fairly even course. However, on reaching a small hummock about 800 feet from take-off, the biplane started pitching again and darted suddenly into the sand. The front rudder frame was damaged badly, but the main frame came through wonderfully well. The flight mark was 852 feet in 59 seconds, in which time their engine had made 1071 revolutions.

The great dream of centuries at last had come true. The Wrights had won the great air race. The honor had come to the United States. The date: December 17, 1903.

No Prophets in Their Own Land

The aeroplane was carried back in triumph to the level area near the shed, and while the men stood around discussing the events of the day, a sudden gust of wind started to turn the light machine over. All hands rushed to save it, and Wilbur who was near a wingtip ran to the front rudders, but could not apply his weight in time. Daniels and Orville tried to grab spars at the rear, but were too late to have any effect, and the machine went over on its back. Daniels, who was not too familiar with the structure tried to throw himself over the lower wing, and became entangled in the propellers and drive chains, but suffered no serious injury. The engine legs were broken off, the chain guides were badly bent, a number of interplane struts and many ribs were broken. After a complete examination was made, it was decided that one of the main spars was also broken.

It was obvious that no more flying could be attempted that season, so the machine was dismantled, and what could be salvaged was sent back to Dayton where it was stacked in the cellar of the bicycle shop, remaining there for several years.

Although they had made a world-staggering effort to solve at last the problem of mechanical flight, it must be said that neither brother did much about calling attention to their accomplishment. Orville did wire home, stating simply that they had actually flown, and adding that they were making every effort to be home for the Christmas dinner. This telegram was taken to the office of the Dayton *Journal* by their brother Lorin, but Frank Tunison, city editor and also a representative of the Associated Press, said that a flight of less than a minute was not a worthy news item, and was plainly annoyed with such nonsense. So no reference of the world's first powered flight, accomplished by a couple of local young men, appeared in the *Journal* the next day.

However, a long, fanciful story of the Wrights' first flights was sent out from Norfolk, Virginia, by Harry P. Moore of the *Virginian-Pilot*. It appeared in that paper, the Cincinnati *Enquirer*, and some other papers on the morning of December 18, 1903. The manner in which this information got out was explained later by Orville who said that late in the afternoon of December 17 he and Wilbur walked over to Kitty Hawk, four miles away, to send home the telegram telling of their success. The only telegraph available was at the Weather Bureau station, and the wire was sent over the Weather Bureau line to the station in Norfolk, and there transferred to the Western Union circuit.

While they were still at the Kitty Hawk station, James J. Gray, a Weather Bureau man at Norfolk, asked permission to give the news to a newspaperman friend of his. The Wrights politely said "no," but Gray ignored their refusal, and advised Harry P. Moore who in turn tried to get some details of the flights by telephone. Failing in that, he manufactured a highly colored version of the events that appeared the next day. When an account of the flights was offered in the *Enquirer*, the Dayton *Journal* staff realized that something important had happened and they had missed the story.

Years later, Fred C. Kelly, who was entrusted with editing the letters of the Wright brothers, tried to run this whole story down. Keville Glennan, one-time editor of the *Virginian-Pilot*, told him that he remembered that the Wright telegram had been seen by Ed Dean who regularly covered the Weather Bureau, and who had been told of the flights by a friend in that office. Glennan and Dean then worked for several hours trying to obtain more details and had a short report ready to put into type when Moore appeared and asked if they knew about the Wrights' story. At the time Moore was not a regular reporter but was actually working in the paper's business office. Although Moore's account was on the fantastic and broadly imaginative side, it must be admitted that it resulted in headlining the story.

A few hours after this intercepted wire got out, the Norfolk correspondent of the New York *World* wired for exclusive rights to pictures and story. Awaiting a contract on this, the *World* asked for a six-hundred-word story of the flight. The *Woman's Home Companion* requested pictures, as did *Scientific American,* but what resulted from these inquiries has never been clearly explained. What reports were "ghosted" and published all seemed to take the attitude that it was all very humorous—and probably a great hoax. Weeks later, many European papers were treating the sparse reports of the Wrights' flight with derisive skepticism and aeronauts were advised to "Stick to your balloons and dirigibles! The Wrights? A pair of precious Yankee crackpots. No one can seriously believe they have flown."

For much of this, the Wrights themselves were somewhat to blame, for at times they displayed a fanatical determination to perfect their machine, and fear of ridicule and a natural desire to protect their invention, on a businesslike basis, made them shun publicity. In fact, Wilbur Wright stated in 1906: "We will make no exhibition test of our flying machine, nor permit an examination of it. Neither is necessary for our purpose. Those with whom we are negotiating are satisfied it does all we claim. Our only market must be a powerful government, and publicity would seem to defeat our purpose to make such a sale. We do not need newspapers to tell us of our successes, for we, and those whom we desire, know we have accomplished all we claim." Only practical men with the true independent spirit could have taken this baffling attitude.

Senator Henry Cabot Lodge, advised of the Wrights' flights by Boston businessman Godfrey Cabot, suggested that the War Department buy up the Wrights' invention, but nothing was done about it. Then Augustus M. Herring, who had defected from the Montgomery team, wrote to the Wrights, explaining that he, too, had invented a successful aeroplane some time previously, and wanted to join forces with them, taking a one-third interest. They were to have considerable trouble with Mr. Herring.

CHAPTER IV

The Experiment Continues

Santos-Dumont Flies Again • If War Comes • The
Flight of the Farman • The Aerial Experiment Associa-
tion • Selfridge's First Flight • Canada Takes to the
Air • McCurdy's Great Flight

Only mildly elated with their solution of the secret of mechanical flight, the Wright brothers returned to
Dayton in time to join their family for the Christmas holidays, taking but a small fraction of time to jot down a few
notes and fill in the data of the record of their experiments.
Their success yielded no immediate financial reward, but
the bicycle shop still brought in about $3000 a year, so after
the holidays they started construction on a new, greater-
powered biplane, and made a deal with Torrence Huffman,
a Dayton banker, to use part of his farm at Huffman Prairie,
Simms Station, eight miles outside of Dayton, for further
flying activity the following spring.

From this point on, until they made a series of flying
exhibitions for European authorities in 1908, the Wrights,
to all intents and purposes, dropped out of sight as far as

American interest was concerned. Yet during the year 1904 they made 105 flights at Huffman Prairie, including several five-minute efforts, and logged forty-five minutes of actual flying time. This does not seem like much, but the knowledge and experience gained were of great importance.

But who witnessed any of these early aeroplane flights? What fortunate people actually saw any of these historic events? Amazingly, only a few local farm workers, and passengers on an interurban trolley line that passed their flying field. Now and then a picnic party, out for an afternoon, may have heard a Wright biplane clattering over their heads, but no newsman ever tried to find out what was going on at Huffman Prairie, and as the flights continued and lengthened, the Wrights decided not to invite members of the press. They just continued their work, keeping most of the details of their machines secret for the time being. They had some general idea of what they had accomplished and what they had contributed to the science, but years later Orville admitted that had anyone offered them $10,000 for all rights to their invention they would have accepted with gratitude.

During the early part of 1905 they succeeded in making a circular flight covering more than three miles around their Huffman Prairie field, and had attained a speed of 35 miles an hour. This new success inspired the idea that the aeroplane could play a major part in preventing wars because it would permit each side to know what the other was doing, and thus make it more difficult for the other to gain a strategic advantage. With this military factor in mind, the Wrights got in touch with Robert M. Nevin, the Congressional representative from their district, asking him to determine whether the United States government was in any way interested in their machine. After some delay, it was learned through routine channels that "no allotments have been made for the experimental development of devices for mechanical flight," and that "the device must have been brought to the stage of practical operation without expense to the United States before any official action could be taken."

In other words, the United States government was interested only in a machine that would fly—one that had proved its ability.

In contrast, Colonel J. E. Capper of the British Royal Aircraft Factory had called on the Wrights in October 1904, and stated openly that he was seeing them at the request of His Majesty's government, and before leaving he asked them to make his government a bona fide proposal for the sale of one of their machines or the manufacturing rights. On learning of this, Octave Chanute wrote to Wilbur:

My first feelings were of mortification and regret that the United States War Department should have extended to you a flat "turn down" as you express it. Now that I have cooled down I see some advantages in your being forced to consider the overtures made by Colonel Capper for the British government, because: First, your invention is worth far more to the British than to the United States government. Second, the British are less hampered than we in appropriating secret service funds, so you can probably get a better price, and sooner. Third, your invention will make more for peace in the hands of the British than in our own, for its existence will soon become known in a general way and the knowledge will deter embroilments.

Ironically, nine years later, the British Royal Flying Corps was sending three military air squadrons across the English Channel to fight the first war in the air.

In late 1905 the United States government was still taking the stand that the Wrights would have to offer "a machine which by actual operation is shown to be able to produce

horizontal flight and carry an operator." By that time the
Wrights had made one circular flight of 25¼ miles, remaining in the air for 38 minutes, 3 seconds. All their activities
were still taking place on a pasture bordered by two high-
ways and an interurban trolley line, but no newspapermen
from Dayton or any other city in the United States bothered to take note of them. What price American initiative?
Not one word of their efforts appeared anywhere—except in
one or two European journals and even these were read
with considerable doubt and much questioning.

Santos-Dumont Flies Again

The portent of the Wright conquest, stimulated by a few
vague but intriguing reports of their continued success,
aroused new interest in powered flight in Europe, but it
was not until October 1906, almost three years after the
Wrights skimmed over the dunes at Kitty Hawk, that a
European aeronaut could claim success in this new field.
The ambitious airman was none other than Alberto Santos-
Dumont, the Brazilian-Parisian who had flown a small dirigible around the Eiffel Tower in 1901.

Desirous of becoming a heavier-than-air pilot, Santos-
Dumont first equipped a Hargrave box kite, built by the
Voisin brothers, with an 8-cylinder, 50-horsepower *Antoinette* engine, a type he had been using in his airships. This
machine which he called the "14-Bis" was hauled to the
Bagatelle cavalry field on August 22, 1906, and fastened to
the framework of his Number 14 dirigible. The idea was
to take the powered machine into the air, release it, and
fly it back to earth under its own power. Once it was free,
the Hargrave machine worked very well, and Santos-Du-

mont landed it safely, but the effort scarcely could be called an acceptable heavier-than-air flight.

The trial, however, had satisfied the Brazilian aeronaut that his machine could be handled under power, flown through a few primary maneuvers, and brought safely back to earth. Encouraged by this, Santos-Dumont next planned to make a conventional aeroplane flight with the same machine. His Hargrave aircraft came to be known as a *canard* because although it was of standard biplane construction, its fuselage jutted out forward from the main wings, supporting a large control assembly, making it appear to be flying backward. The engine was mounted between the wings, and the propeller twirled as a pusher. Two bicycle wheels, set in standard cycle forks, were mounted as the landing gear directly under the pilot's nacelle just forward of the leading edges of the wings.

On September 7, 1906, Santos-Dumont risked his first powered flight, taking off from the Bagatelle field, but his wheels left the ground for only an instant. He tried again on September 13, covering about 30 yards at a height of three feet, but by October 23 he had flown his *canard* a distance of 200 feet at a speed of 25 miles an hour. For this effort he won a prize of 3000 francs, offered by Ernest Archdeacon, a Parisian sportsman who had put up the sum three years before for the first man to fly a distance of 25 meters. Again, no one had taken the trouble to check on the report that the Wrights had flown a distance of 852 feet in 1903.

Unquestionably, the Santos-Dumont machine was a freak device with no commercial future, but it had flown, and the Brazilian was fascinated with it. After his flight on October 23 he modified the 14-Bis and added a set of ailerons to furnish some lateral control, and on November 12 he made several more attempts to fly it. In one effort he got the machine up to 15 feet and continued on in straight flight until he saw he was running out of aerodrome space. He tried to make a turn, but lost flying speed, nosed down, and for a minute seemed to be heading for a serious crash. The new ailerons, however, enabled him to get a wing down in time to take the full shock on the wingtip. The whole lifting surface was damaged seriously, but the pilot was uninjured. In this instance Santos-Dumont had covered a distance of 722 feet in 21½ seconds.

If War Comes

After reading of Santos-Dumont's flight the next morning, November 13, Lord Northcliffe, owner of London's *Daily Mail,* was angered that his editor has missed the full significance of the flight. From his home he raged over the telephone: "Santos-Dumont flies 722 feet. Don't you realize that England no longer is an island? Let me tell you, there will be no more sleeping safely behind the wooden walls of old England with the Channel our safety moat. This means aerial chariots of a foe will descend on British soil if war comes!"

The next edition of the *Daily Mail* carried the following editorial:

The time is probably near at hand in which aerial motor-cars will become the playthings of the rich. We know by experience that this stage of development will be followed by one in which the new appliances will be commercially utilized. All the conditions of life will then be revolutionised. Roads will become unnecessary when it becomes possible to voyage through space. The air around London and other large cities will be darkened by the flight of aeroplanes. New difficulties of every kind will arise, not the least being the military problem caused by the virtual annihilation of frontiers and the acquisition of power to pass readily through the air above the sea. The isolation of the United Kingdom may disappear and thus the success of M. Santos-Dumont has an international significance. They are not mere dreamers who hold that the time is at hand when air power will be an even more important thing than sea power.

The wings of war were sprouting their pin feathers.

In the face of this ominous prediction, aeroplane enthusiasts in Great Britain were cognizant of their impotence, and failure to produce one practical heavier-than-air machine, and there were some foreigners who flung chauvinistic taunts, adding that England was waiting to reap the fruits of some other nations's brains. To counter this, Lord Northcliffe startled the aviation world on November 17, 1906, with an offer of £10,000 (about $50,000 at that time) for the first flight from London to Manchester. The offer read in part:

The proprietors of the *Daily Mail* therefore undertake to pay the sum of £10,000 to the first person being a member of an established aero club who flies in one day from a given spot within five miles of the London office of the *Daily Mail* to a given spot within five miles of the Manchester office of the *Daily Mail.* This offer is made without conditions or restrictions of any kind except those mentioned. We insist upon an aeroplane being the only practical machine for flight.

This was the first of many such prizes offered by Lord Northcliffe to encourage the development of aviation. He hoped to inspire British pioneers of whom so little was being heard, and to assist them to catch up with the progress being made in other countries. Many people ridiculed the *Daily Mail's* offer and considered it cheap publicity. The magazine *Punch* found many opportunities to present typical jokes and cartoons deriding the offers, and a current limerick of the day ran:

> There was a young man of Park Lane
> Who constructed a new aeroplane;
> It flew, so we heard,
> Like a beautiful bird,
> His tombstone was pretty, but plain.

Few readers of the *Daily Mail* believed, or realized that the prize for the London-to-Manchester flight would be won within four years.

The Flight of the Farman

Early in April 1906 a French military delegation, which had been instructed to make a deal with the Wrights, arrived in Dayton. In the delegation were a Captain Fournier, military attaché at Washington, and a Mr. Berry, official legal adviser to the French embassy. Earlier that year a French syndicate, hoping to gain manufacturing rights to the Wright machine, agreed to post a forfeit of 25,000 francs by February 9, and to deposit an additional 1,000,000 francs in a New York bank before April 5; of which 750,000 francs were to be paid to the Wrights as soon as they delivered a machine. According to the contract, this machine was to be flown on a trial flight of 50 kilometers (about 31 miles), and the balance of the money was to be theirs after an interval, not exceeding three months more, during which time the Wrights were to give instructions in assembling the aeroplane, and in flying it.

An Austrian aero association also made a proposal to purchase a Wright biplane that was to be offered to Emperor Franz Josef on the occasion of his Sixtieth Jubilee in 1908.

The French offer, however, was allowed to languish, because the would-be purchasers insisted later that the plane fly at an altitude of 300 meters, or about a thousand feet. The Wrights did not care to consider such a stipulation with a contract limit of August 1 facing them. They felt that there was not enough time for preliminary practice, or to assure that their newest machine was capable of such altitude.

By this time, too, the Wrights felt that Captain Ferdinand Ferber, a glider enthusiast and head of France's military aviation operations, was convinced that he could build a machine that would equal any flights the Wrights had made. In fact, Ferber was determined that his country would soon lead the world in heavier-than-air flight, and was more than willing to risk voiding any contract with the Wrights to do so.

Many of Ferber's hopes were raised late in 1907 when France scored a new victory. Henri Farman, son of a transplanted Britisher, flew a Voisin biplane a distance of 770 meters (about 2300 feet) at a speed greater than 50 miles an hour. This flight was made at Issy-les-Moulineaux, and far exceeded Santos-Dumont's record of 20 meters. All of France went wild once more, and Captain Ferber was convinced that they could get along without any help from the Wrights.

Henri (sometimes spelled Henry) Farman was one of three sons of Richard Farman, British correspondent in Paris for the *Daily Telegram*. Henri, Maurice, and Richard were born in Paris of direct British descent, and although they did not adopt French citizenship until late in life, they were basically French in education, manners, and viewpoint. Henri studied painting and was exceptionally good. He was also a champion tandem cyclist with his brother

Maurice. On the other hand, Dick was an automobile enthusiast, and as early as 1896 had written a book about motorcars. Maurice devoted his time to astronomy, meteorology, and ballooning. Henri, however, was the first to take up heavier-than-air flying. He bought a Voisin biplane in 1907 and learned to fly at Issy-les-Moulineaux where Gabriel and Charles Voisin, pioneer French experimenters, had set up a factory and flying field. Gabriel had engaged in the sport very early, and was renowned for his model aeroplanes. The two brothers had founded their factory in 1905, and between the years 1906–13 constructed numerous experimental machines including their famous Voisin box kite upon which many airmen learned to fly.

After his first epic flight, Henri Farman became a national hero in France, and on January 13, 1908, surpassed everything that had been accomplished in Europe.

In 1907, possibly inspired by Farman's feat, Henri Deutsche de la Murthe, a sportsman and industrialist, and the aforementioned Ernest Archdeacon, put up a prize of 50,000 francs for the first person to fly 500 meters straightaway, turn in the air, and return to the starting point to complete a closed kilometer flight.

No one remembered, or had the courage to remind the donors, that the Wrights had already flown circuits covering more than 24 miles. It must be admitted that the two Dayton fliers had done little to spread the accounts of their efforts. It is true that they had told official organizations of their work, and had given full details of their flights and the names of reliable Americans who had witnessed these flights, but apparently no one in Europe seemed to be impressed or convinced. It was not until August 1908 when Wilbur Wright put on his first display at Le Mans, France, that Europe, or for that matter the United States, had any conception of what had been going on at Huffman Prairie.

So Henri Farman, the leading airman in Europe, on January 12, convoked the official committee of the Aero Club of France to witness his trial that was to take place the following day. The next morning dawned fine and calm, and at 10:00 A.M. Farman took off gracefully from the Army drill field at Issy-les-Moulineaux and raced on for the 500-meter mark. Making a sweeping turn around this, he flew straight back to the starting flag.

Another great triumph of the skies had been chalked up to the French, and Henri Farman had 50,000 francs with which to open an aircraft factory of his own. That same year he built his own pusher biplane that was fitted with a set of wing flaps to provide lateral control. He captured several lucrative prizes with this machine, always under the watchful eye of the French Aero Club officials. In fact, Henri soon had a number of respectable records to his credit.

The Farman machines were so successful Henri and Maurice were induced to set up a factory in Bradford, England, to supply the British Army with some equipment that would fly. Maurice undertook the drawing-board work, Henri built the machines, and Dick handled the business end of the project. At Bradford, and at their factory at Billancourt, outside Paris, the Farman brothers eventually turned out 1084 of their primitive pushers for the British Royal Flying Corps, and many of these aerial dreadnoughts stayed in the service until well into 1916. The Farman Shorthorn biplanes of Number 4 Squadron that arrived in France early in September 1914 were the first active-service aircraft that were definitely equipped for aerial combat. They were indeed armed with a Lewis gun, but, amusingly enough, the machines would not leave the ground if gunners were included in the payload.

Other French airmen were also turning out some commendable machines. Robert Esnault-Pelterie produced in 1907 his R.E.P. monoplane in which the wings were designed on the cantilever theory, and were strong enough to withstand heavy strain in the air without exterior bracing wires. Esnault-Pelterie was years ahead of the field, for he went into the streamlined idea long before the sleek monoplanes of later years appeared on the scene. He also introduced new designs in wheeled landing gears.

Léon Delagrange, French sculptor-inventor, was another outstanding figure of the time who performed many fine feats in a Voisin-type biplane. He was a friendly rival of Henri Farman, and was the first pilot to take a passenger aloft, and followed this by being the first airman to take a woman into the air at Turin, Italy, on July 8, 1908. She was Madame Thérèsè Peltier, another French sculptor. In that same year Delagrange raised the world's record for distance and duration in the air four times in five months. This gallant airman was killed in an accident while flying at Bordeaux in 1910.

The Aerial Experiment Association

The year 1907 was a memorable one in American aviation. America's first air trophy was offered by *Scientific American* magazine, and was to be competed for by any heavier-than-air flying machines displayed at the Jamestown (New York) Exposition. The competition was to be held under the auspices of the Aero Club of America, but when the first contest was called there were no machines capable of flight—the Wrights had not bothered to submit an entry.

The following year another air meet was staged at St. Louis, and the conditions for this competition called for a straightaway flight of one kilometer (3280 feet), and the trophy must have been won three times for permanent possession. The plan was to vary the conditions, and the second competition would require a circular flight. Although the Wrights had flown as early as 1903 and had been making many circuits by 1905, these facts were not generally accepted as yet.

In the meantime, in order to put America's aerial experiments on a businesslike basis, the Aerial Experiment Association, sponsored by Mrs. Alexander Graham Bell, and formed originally at Baddeck, Nova Scotia, was moved to Hammondsport, New York. This note is worth some explanation.

Professor Alexander Graham Bell, a Scotsman by birth and many years a resident of Canada, later adopted American citizenship. Bell had early become interested in the possibilities of flight and at his summer home in Nova Scotia had conducted experiments with large kites of ingenious design in an effort to find what types of lifting surface were most effective. In the course of events he became acquainted with Professor Langley, and the American scientist visited Professor Bell at his home, known as Beinn Bhreagh at Baddeck on the shores of Bras d'Or Lake, Cape Breton, Nova Scotia.

In 1896 Bell visited Langley and was present at Quantico, Virginia, when Langley's steam-driven *Aerodrome* model made a most successful flight. The Scottish scientist was so impressed that he returned to his own efforts with renewed interest. He resumed kite flying again, and in 1899 he read a paper, *Kites with Radial Wings,* that was published in the *National Academy of Science* magazine.

That same year the Wrights had written to the Smithsonian Institution requesting literature on this subject, and in 1902 they published a paper describing their experiments with a wind tunnel. Before that year was out, a Canadian engineer, Wallace Rupert Turnbull, also built a wind tunnel in a large barn adjacent to his home in Rothesay, a short distance from St. John, New Brunswick. Wallace Turnbull, who was trained in mechanical and electrical engineering at Cornell University and at the University of Berlin, Germany, was the first Canadian to tackle the purely theoretical aspects of aeronautics. He produced valuable information on the theory of dihedral angle that must have had a strong influence on subsequent design. The Wrights' great contribution in this work was their data on wing camber, and the determination of the center of pressure.

After Professor Langley's ill fortune on the Potomac, and the refusal of the Wright brothers to make a real effort to prove their claims to heavier-than-air flight, there was a decided letdown in interest in the United States; all activity seemed to be taking place in France and Germany.

Somewhere around 1906 two young Canadians, Frederick W. (Casey) Baldwin and John A. D. McCurdy, were busy completing their engineering course at the University of Toronto. McCurdy's home was at Baddeck, Nova Scotia, where his father had been Professor Bell's secretary. Hearing of Bell's experiments with kites, Casey Baldwin eagerly accepted McCurdy's invitation to spend the summer of 1907 at the Baddeck home. Dr. Bell was more than pleased to have these two young, active men join him. While listening in on their discussions after their kite-flying experiments, Mrs. Bell suggested that they form an organization to put their collective ideas into effect. She offered to finance the cost of such an undertaking, and thus was formed, in an obscure corner of Nova Scotia, the Aerial Experiment Association that became world renowned, and contributed so much to flying.

Professor Bell next invited Glenn Curtiss to join the association, chiefly because of his knowledge of gasoline engines. For the record it should be noted that Curtiss had been in touch with the Wrights as early as May 1906 when he wrote a letter explaining that he was concentrating on the development of lightweight gasoline engines, and wondered if he could be of any assistance to the men who were flying regularly at Huffman Prairie. A few months later, September 1906, Captain Thomas S. Baldwin, noted aeronaut, who was giving exhibition airship flights in Dayton, asked Curtiss to come to that city to make some repairs on the airship's power plant. While this work was being done, the Wrights, Baldwin, and Curtiss had several friendly talks. The Wrights displayed a number of photographs of their flights that had been made over the previous two years.

Glenn Curtiss was somewhat amazed, and immediately became interested in heavier-than-air flight. He asked many pertinent questions, all of which the Wrights answered, but it is generally believed that Curtiss had no intention of taking up powered flight. He was content to design and build engines.

Another American who joined the Aerial Experiment Association was Lieutenant Thomas E. Selfridge of the United States Army whose inclusion was suggested by officials of the United States government who wished to have an observer in the group.

In January 1908 Selfridge wrote to the Wright brothers,

"taking the liberty" of asking for advice on certain points connected with their earlier glider experiments, and for some details on constructing wing ribs, and how the linen was fastened to the wing frames. Again, the Dayton men not only gave their views, but named journals in which their findings had been published. Later on much of this detail, according to the Wrights, was to be found in the famed Curtiss *June Bug* that was flown by Glenn Curtiss at Hammondsport, July 4, 1908, but no credit was given to the Wrights at the time.

Selfridge's First Flight

This international aerial organization made its first actual flight December 6, 1907, with a tetrahedral kite that was designed by Dr. Bell. In it he had arranged a number of triangular lifting surfaces to a series of light frames. (Tetrahedral means "bounded by four triangular surfaces.") Lieutenant Selfridge was selected by lot to go aloft on one of these kites which was named *Cygnet I*. The device was set up on a pair of light pontoons, and was to be airborne by means of a power launch.

Selfridge lay flat on a light framework, and the launch sped forward over the water of Bras d'Or Lake. The Bell kite rose to a height of 168 feet and rode steadily for seven minutes. The kite carried no controls; Selfridge was just a passenger and had to depend on the alertness of a crew member to get back safely on the lake surface. The launch eased down, and the kite glided back to the water, but the crewman who was supposed to cut the kite line with an ax the instant the pontoons touched down, was so engrossed with the display, he forgot to do so, and Selfridge was dragged below the surface of the lake. He was rescued in time, but the big kite was broken up, parts of it being scattered over the water.

Meanwhile, Glenn Curtiss, working in his factory at Hammondsport, New York, had been in charge of designing a biplane glider for the association. Mrs. Bell financed this work, and some successful flights were made in the Lake Keuka area, and following these experiments, the Aerial Experiment Association was moved to Hammondsport. It was here that their first powered plane, called the *Red Wing* because of the color of the fabric used, was built and first flown. All members contributed to this effort, although it has been stated since that the general design was the work of Lieutenant Selfridge. He never flew the *Red Wing*, however. This time the choice fell to Casey Baldwin who was listed as the chief engineer of the project. This biplane was not greatly unlike the Wright machine except that its engine turned only one propeller. The pilot sat on an ordinary kitchen chair that had its legs removed, and was shielded from the wind by a conical fabric-covered framework. The engine was a Curtiss 8-cylindered affair that developed 40 horsepower, and had a carburetor set to serve each cylinder.

On March 12, 1908, the biplane was hauled out to the ice-covered Lake Keuka, and the engine started. The *Red Wing* had no trouble moving off as it was mounted on a skid landing gear. After a short run against a light breeze, Baldwin raised the plane clear of the ice, and it covered 319 feet before he brought it down to a very good landing on the ice. In fact, this was the first publicly announced flight in the United States, and Baldwin was the first British subject ever to fly a heavier-than-air machine.

A short time later Baldwin made a second flight, but after

covering 120 feet the plane went out of control and crashed. The pilot was not injured, but the machine was seriously damaged, so it was decided to dismantle it and develop a new model. The *Red Wing* had no ailerons or lateral control of any kind which undoubtedly contributed to its ill luck. It will be noted that lateral control was the bugaboo of all these pioneer designers, for they had not yet fully appreciated the value of this all-important factor in flight.

On the strength of his experience Casey Baldwin was given the honor of designing the A.E.A.'s second machine, which was called the *White Wing* owing to its light-colored fabric. It was decided that some method of providing lateral control should be considered, and this resulted in an improvement on the Wrights' wing-warping system, and Henri Farman's wing flaps. Two triangular panels were mounted in triangular frames out on the wingtips, and could be operated by the pilot through a shoulder yoke against which he sat. In the Farman biplane these flaps hung loosely until the machine was under way, and when the pilot wished to raise or lower a wingtip he simply lowered the flap that would bring such a response. In the *White Wing* these flaps, or ailerons as they were called, worked in conjunction. When one was lowered by the shoulder yoke, the other was raised, and in that way both wingtips were controlled simultaneously, resulting in faster reaction and greater safety.

This aileron problem, and its various adaptations, was the basis of the long-drawn-out legal battle in the United States courts between the Wright brothers and Glenn Curtiss concerning patent rights on the development of wingtip control. In fact, these lawsuits were still in progress when America entered World War I in 1917. By that time settlement became imperative, and the Wright and Curtiss representatives were brought together and a satisfactory settlement made.

The first flight test of the *White Wing* was made by Baldwin on May 18, 1908, from Stony Brook Farm in Hammondsport, where the Canadian succeeded in covering 279 feet. The next day Lieutenant Selfridge tried his hand and managed about a hundred feet. On a second attempt, Selfridge covered 240 feet. On May 22 Glenn Curtiss climbed into the seat and made 1017 feet on his first try. The next day McCurdy flew the *White Wing* about six hundred feet, and then had an accident on a subsequent take-off that put him on crutches for a short time.

By now the Aerial Experiment Association was enthusiastic over its continuing success, and planned a third model, to be known as the *June Bug*. Its design was credited to Curtiss and became one of the best known in America. McCurdy and Curtiss made some fine flights in it, the longest being on August 29, 1908, when McCurdy flew a distance of two miles. The *June Bug* had already won all hearts when Curtiss flew it over an official one-kilometer flight on July 4, 1908, and was awarded the *Scientific American* trophy. The actual distance flown was 5090 feet in one minute, 42⅕ seconds.

In November 1908 the A.E.A. group modified the *June Bug*, mounted it on a pair of pontoon floats and renamed it *The Loon*. As such it was the first hydro-aeroplane to be built in the United States, but though McCurdy and Curtiss did their best to get her off the water at Lake Keuka, *The Loon* never actually flew, but she was the incentive for many more of the type to come from the Curtiss factory.

Canada Takes to the Air

A complete history of Canadian aviation makes fascinating reading, for few people realize how significant Canada's contribution to the development of flying has been. We have seen how Casey Baldwin became the first British subject to fly a heavier-than-air machine, and the progress made by John A. D. McCurdy under the guidance of Glenn Curtiss. As a member of the Aerial Experiment Association, McCurdy contributed handsomely, and after his valiant attempts to get *The Loon* to fly, he turned his attention to designing the association's fourth powered biplane.

This was the famous *Silver Dart,* one of the finest pioneer machines built at the time. It had a wingspan of 49 feet with a center chord of six feet, tapering at the tips to four feet. Fully loaded with a pilot aboard the *Silver Dart* weighed 800 pounds, and, of course, was powered with one of the Glenn Curtiss engines. This plant, instead of being air-cooled as were the previous types, was water-cooled, and might be considered the first successful engine of its type in the world—that is to say, unless the Wrights' engine is to be considered an out-and-out aviation power plant. The *Dart's* engine developed 35 horsepower at 1000 revolutions per minute, and turned a pusher propeller that was carved out of a single balk of timber. The drive was not direct from the crankshaft, but the prop speed was cut to the ratio of 18/24 by a belt and pulley system.

McCurdy first flew the *Silver Dart* at Hammondsport where he guided it over a distance of 600 feet on December

Eugene Lefebvre, popular French airman shown flying a 1909 Wright
plane at Reims. His specialty was 40-mph power dives against cavalry
oops and chasing press photographers about the flying field. Lefebvre was
lled a short time after this picture was taken, while testing a new Wright
plane.

. The early problems of flight. Lieutenant Kennedy of the British Army
rns to glide at a meeting of the Hants Aero Club at Fort Grange. This
cture was taken in April 1910 and shows how forward propulsion was
tablished in those days.

Air-Britain Digest Photo

11. A hot weekend at Blackpool! Louis Paulhan, French airman who w. to win the *Daily Mail's* London-to-Manchester flight, is shown passing pylon in his Farman biplane. Picture was taken on October 20, 1909.

12. One of the best photograp pre-World War I flying. Here i Van der Borren flying a Farma plane at the Nice meeting hel April 1910. He is shown comir for a landing a few feet above beach.

Air-Britain Digest Photo

Louis Paulhan, noted French airman flying in the first Reims meet in
9. Originally a mechanic, he won a Voisin biplane minus its engine in a
vspaper competition. Friends chipped in and bought him a power plant
l Paulhan taught himself to fly. He was to become one of the world's
st famous pilots.

14. Another version of the 1910 aero sport. Here a would-be pilot gets
a feel of the air by taking his first lesson aboard a glider which is being
pulled and flown as a kite.

15. Early U.S. Navy aviation training. Glenn Curtiss, left, gives flying instructions to Lieutenant John Towers in 1910 aboard a Curtiss biplane of the period. Towers went on to become an admiral and head all U.S. Navy operations.

16. Eugene Ely after his successful landing aboard USS *Pennsylvania* (January 19, 1911) prepares to fly off and return to shore. In this picture will be seen the undercarriage hooks used to grab the arrester-gear ropes stretched across the deck.

5, 1908. Before Christmas Day had arrived, he had made ten more flights of varying distances.

After these exploits, Dr. Bell was anxious to have one of the A.E.A. machines perform in Canada, and late in February 1909 the *Dart* was shipped to Baddeck, and Canadian aviation history was inaugurated when McCurdy flew the machine more than half a mile over the frozen surface of Bras d'Or Lake, establishing the first heavier-than-air flight in Canada. This, also, was the first controlled flight of an aeroplane by a British subject at any point in the British Commonwealth.

John McCurdy was now one of the most skilled pilots in the world, and on March 10, 1909, he flew the *Silver Dart* on a circular course, covering a distance of 20 miles. In the following months the *Dart* logged more than 2000 miles.

Having accomplished their prime mission—to design, build, and fly a heavier-than-air machine that would sustain a pilot in controlled flight—the Aerial Experiment Association disbanded in March 1909, and the members went their various ways. Baldwin and McCurdy remained associates at Baddeck where they built two more biplanes, listed as *Baddeck I* and *Baddeck II*, both of which were flown regularly with great success.

McCurdy and Baldwin were so pleased with their efforts they approached the Canadian government with the idea of proving the military value of their machines. They appear to be the first airmen to offer to make tests with their aircraft and to show that the aeroplane had a vital place in national defense. But the military authorities had little use for these noisy contraptions; anything mechanical was beyond their understanding, and it was not until a Major Maunsell, Director of Engineering Services in Canada, showed some interest that the two men from Nova Scotia were invited to display their machines before a military committee. The *Silver Dart* was shipped from Baddeck to the Petawawa military camp northwest of Ottawa.

Flying from the level meadows of Hammondsport, or off the smooth ice of Bras d'Or Lake had been fairly simple, but the ground at Petawawa was sandy, uneven, and unfitted for operations of aircraft of that day. The wheels of the *Silver Dart* had narrow bicycle tires not more than two inches in diameter, and the aircraft had great difficulty in gaining take-off speed, but more important, both McCurdy and Baldwin were aboard, sitting in a tight tandem arrangement to prove that their machine could carry a pilot and a military observer. Despite these difficulties, four successful flights were made on August 2, 1909, just seven days after Louis Blériot had completed his historic crossing of the English Channel.

On the fifth flight, with McCurdy piloting the *Silver Dart*, the landing had to be made dead into the glare of the lowering sun, and it was difficult to pick out the best area. One of the wheels struck a light rise of sand. The machine was swung sharply, a wingtip dug in, and the whole right wing section was torn clear of the framework. McCurdy and Baldwin were partly covered with debris but neither received serious injury. The crackup marked the end of the *Silver Dart*.

Fortunately, *Baddeck II* had also been shipped on from Nova Scotia, and by August 12 that machine was ready for flight. Once more, they made four very satisfactory flights before a large throng of military observers, but again, the fifth proved their undoing; their biplane was badly damaged as the result of another rough landing. That was enough for the Canadian military authorities, and the demonstrations were terminated.

As a footnote to this, it is interesting to observe that Canada did not make any further strides toward a military air arm until September 16, 1914, when the first Canadian Air Corps was born. This organization was conceived by Colonel Sam Hughes, then Minister of Defense, who at the time was engaged in assembling the First Canadian contingent at Valcartier Camp near Quebec. He was determined that the Canadian Expeditionary Force should have its own Aviation Corps, and overnight appointed a provisional commander, E. L. Janney, commissioned him a captain, and authorized him to spend up to $5000 for a military aircraft. Someone in the United States provided a machine for exactly that amount, and it was flown to Valcartier where it was taken apart and crated for shipment overseas. In October it accompanied Canada's 1st Division to Britain, and was dumped on Salisbury Plain. It never again took to the air, but was left standing in the mud near the famed Stonehenge monuments. It eventually was sold for scrap.

The *Silver Dart* and *Baddeck I* were shipped back to Nova Scotia, and the engine of the *Silver Dart* was relegated to furnish power for a motor launch. Some years later the launch became water-logged, and sank. The hull and its historic engine lay beneath the surface for many months. The engine was recovered later, finally cleaned up and placed in the Canadian Aeronautical Museum of the National Research Council in Ottawa.

Disappointed, but undismayed, McCurdy and Baldwin continued their work as the Canadian Aerodrome Company, and on March 7, 1910, McCurdy flew the *Baddeck II* a distance of more than 20 miles in 16 minutes, and in that same year won the world's biplane speed record at the Second International Aviation Meet at Belmont Park, New York. On August 27, during a flight from Sheepshead Bay,

Long Island, McCurdy tapped out the first wireless message to be sent from an aeroplane to a ground station. By this time Casey Baldwin had given up active flying to concentrate on the theoretical aspects of flight, particularly in the field of hydrofoils for waterborne aircraft; data that became valuable to Canada's bush pilots some two decades later.

McCurdy's Great Flight

In order to bolster their finances, McCurdy competed in exhibitions and prize ventures that were offering lucrative rewards. On January 31, 1911, he assembled a new Curtiss biplane on a beach at Key West, Florida, to make a flight to Havana, Cuba. This was a risky venture, for it meant a nonstop flight over 95 miles of shark-infested water that separated the Florida Keys from Cuba, but there was a prize of $10,000 for the first airman to complete such a flight.

McCurdy took off with the intention of making a test flight to check his engine and the plane's controls, but his wheels had no sooner left the ground than spectators swarmed over the area from where he had taken off. There was no practical way in which to warn them of his return, so he accepted the situation, turned the nose of his plane and headed for Havana.

The weather was favorable, and the engine performed well. Within a short time he was within ten miles of the Cuban coast. Giving his few instruments a last inspection, he was startled to see the needle of his oil-pressure gauge slowly sinking to the zero mark. The coastline was clearly in view, but he knew that it was only a matter of minutes before his engine would seize up and stop. When he was over the Straits of Florida and only a mile off shore, the engine quit cold, and he had to glide down with a dead propeller, and hope for a lucky "ditching." Fortunately, he had two light metal tanks lashed to the underside of the lower wings, and these were sufficient to keep him afloat until his escort vessel, USS *Paulding*, came up and fished him out of the water.

The *Paulding* took McCurdy ashore where he was received with wild acclaim, despite his ill luck. Later on at a banquet in his honor in Havana, the President of Cuba presented him with a silver trophy, and a ribbon-bedecked envelope that was supposed to contain the prize of $10,000, but when the Canadian airman returned to his hotel room and opened the gaudy container, he found it stuffed with a wad of newspaper pages cut to the size of American bills. When he returned to the banquet room to pick up his silver trophy, that, too, had vanished.

By 1916 McCurdy developed a defect in vision, and he ceased active flying. He had made a splendid contribution to Canada's history, to say nothing of the fact that he was one of the British Empire's foremost pilots, and among the first to receive a Fédération Aéronautique Internationale license. He is now living in quiet retirement in Montreal, after a full life devoted to aviation, and one tour of duty as lieutenant governor of his native province, Nova Scotia.

CHAPTER V

The Rise of Glenn Curtiss

The Wrights Maintain Their Lead • Success Before the Skeptics • The Death of Lieutenant Selfridge • British Interest • Another Flying School

---

Glenn Curtiss who played such an important role in American aviation, was, like the Wright brothers, a self-taught mechanic. He was born in Hammondsport, New York, in 1878, and in his early teens opened a bicycle shop that was later enlarged into a motorcycle factory. His light power plants, designed expressly for motorcycles, resulted in much attention and a good income. As stated before, it was his experience with gasoline engines that brought him to the notice of Dr. Bell and the Aerial Experiment Association.

By 1908 Glenn Curtiss had sufficient knowledge to design, build, and fly his own machine, and in that year won the *Scientific American* trophy for his flight over the straight-away kilometer with the *June Bug* biplane. On May 1, 1910, he staged what up to then was the most spectacular flight in American aviation when he flew from Albany to New York City, making most of the trip over the Hudson River. That flight probably aroused more American interest in flying than any event up to that time.

Taking off from a field outside Albany, he made his first stop at Poughkeepsie. He took off again, circled the Military Academy at West Point, continued on at heights between 300 and 1000 feet and landed at Inwood to replenish his oil supply, and then went on to New York where crowds of people saw his little plane in the air and screamed their welcome. When Curtiss landed he delivered a letter from the mayor of Albany to Mayor William J. Gaynor of New York City. This was the first long-distance flight in the Western Hemisphere. It covered 142½ miles in 2 hours and 50 minutes of flying time. Curtiss won the New York *World's* prize of $10,000, and in flying over the West Point parade ground, he, like McCurdy and Baldwin, had sown another seed in the sparse garden of military aviation.

The year before Curtiss had established the first flying school in the United States from which many noted aviators were to graduate and enter the prize lists, building up interest in the new science. One of these was Charles E. Hamilton, generally considered the first true cross-country flier in America. In 1910 Hamilton won a prize of $10,000 for flying from New York to Philadelphia in 3 hours, 27 minutes of flying time. Clifford B. Harmon, international sportsman, was also a Curtiss pupil who won the Harvard Cup at the Boston Aviation Meet in 1910, and then completed a flight across Long Island Sound. Eugene Ely who made the first landing on a battleship (1911) was another alumnus of the Curtiss school.

The Wrights also conducted a flying school to provide pilots for this new industry. Their first site was selected at

Montgomery, Alabama, early in 1910 where the climate was more favorable for preliminary flying. Today, their old field is known as Maxwell Air Force Base, and for a number of years was the home of the United States Air Force's Air University. The first pilot taught by the Wrights was Walter Brookins of Dayton, an especial friend of the family. Walter then took over the Montgomery school and among his first class of students was Archie Hoxsey, one of the most personable airmen of that time—the dandy of the barnstorming circuits. Another such charmer was Spencer C. Crane.

After turning over the Montgomery school to Brookins, Orville next opened a flying school at Huffman Prairie where A. L. Welsh and Duval La Chapelle took their tickets. Walter Brookins joined the Ohio school in May and trained Ralph Johnstone and Frank T. Coffyn. Two other candidates who completed the course at the time were Phil O. Parmalee and C. O. Turpin.

It can be seen from this that heavier-than-air flying was spreading from the hands of the original designers, and being taken up by men of many callings, professions, and stations in life.

Another aeronaut of the time was Dr. William W. Christmas of Washington, D.C. who claimed to be the third man in the United States to make a public flight in an aeroplane. Dr. Christmas was for a long time a controversial figure in American aviation, but there is no doubt that on March 8, 1908, or four days before the first flight of the Curtiss *Red Wing*, he flew a pusher biplane of his own design at Fairfax City, Virginia.

The most interesting feature of Dr. Christmas's machine is that unquestionably it was the first American aeroplane to be fitted with ailerons for lateral control that were a hinged portion of the wingtips, just as they are employed today. The Wrights had used the wing-warping system, and Curtiss had continued with the triangular panels mounted in the framework on the outer wingtips. Curtiss later set these controls halfway between the wings, and mounted them on the interplane struts. Dr. Christmas's biplane had no front elevator assembly, as used by the Wrights and Curtiss. The elevators were mounted as an integral part of the tail assembly, as they are on conventional planes today. In fact, it was Dr. Christmas who was recognized as the inventor of the hinged aileron; his patent was validated, and purchased by the United States government for use on all aircraft manufactured during World War I, although both Curtiss and the Wright brothers had for years been claiming priority for the same type of device.

Dr. Christmas was interested in flying as a young boy, and spent much time watching the evolutions of large birds. He had a lengthy correspondence with M. Alexandre G. Eiffel, the French engineer who built the Eiffel Tower, and he made kites, model aeroplanes, and gliders. He built a tandem monoplane glider and gave a public exhibition with it in 1905 from the base of the Washington Monument. Some years later he developed a cantilevered biplane. It is unfortunate that aviation history has given so little space in its records to Dr. Christmas's contribution to the science.

The Wrights Maintain Their Lead

But much of this is getting ahead of the story. We have seen that no one anywhere by 1907 had surpassed the flights being made by the Wrights at Huffman Prairie, and their efforts still were supreme. In France, Henri Farman was being complimented and rewarded for mere hops of one kilometer. The Aerial Experiment Association was only practicing with a biplane glider from a hill outside Hammondsport, and even Dr. Christmas did not make a powered flight until March 1908. Santos-Dumont was revising his ideas about *canard* box kites, and Delagrange and Jules Vuia were still experimenting with new designs. No one had come anywhere near the Wrights' almost daily flights outside Dayton.

Why these two brothers persisted in their almost secret operations may be difficult to understand, except for the fact that they were both self-effacing, quiet, and adverse to publicity. But they were businesslike enough to know that they were years ahead of any other experimenters, and were certain that no one would be able to match their efforts for some years. They were, it must be admitted, suspicious of most visitors, especially those who appeared to have clear ideas of the science, for they felt that they had several valuable and important features in their successful biplane. But they were not shrewd enough to know how to protect themselves. They had experienced considerable trouble in the tangle of red tape in the U. S. Patent Office, and when the United States government made overtures for a possible contract for the delivery of a biplane for military purposes, the wording of the specifications usually confounded them, or the requirements were impossible to fulfill. For instance, there was a matter of posting a bond equal to the amount of the bid to be filed, a factor that troubled them as they did not know if they would have to forfeit the bond, if one or two requirements could not be filled. There were liabilities—and wordy verbiage—that puzzled or distressed them, and amid these negotiations they knew that they still had to protect what they considered their secret developments.

Tormented with bureaucratic opposition, and facing the growing popularity of Glenn Curtiss, who was being patronized to a great extent by top officials of the Smithsonian Institution and the Aero Club of America, the Wrights came to the conclusion that they stood a better chance of recognition abroad. And to this end they completed a new passenger-carrying biplane in 1907, one with a regular seating accommodation in which both the pilot and passenger sat upright on the leading edge of the lower wing. They had increased the horsepower, and with this model prepared to capture the European market.

The main purpose was to fulfill a contract drawn by a French syndicate, headed by M. Lazare-Weiller, a banker who planned to launch a European company and manufacture the Wright biplane for the commercial market. Wilbur and Orville packed the new plane in a crate, and sailed from New York in May. In Paris they became associated with an American financier, Hart O. Berg, who planned to handle the negotiations. In this instance, however, the Wrights' openhanded approach to the business was too simple and direct for the French syndicate, and the discussions were broken off. The 1907 *Flyer*, still in its crate, was stored in a dockside warehouse at Le Havre while the Wrights visited England and Germany without any important business transactions being completed.

Thus, another year passed with no financial reward, but in 1908 the Lazare-Weiller syndicate made a new offer, the terms of which were stringent, but the Wrights felt they could complete them. The contract required that the aeroplane, carrying a pilot and passenger (or ballast in lieu of one) must, on a date chosen by Mr. Wright, fly 50 kilometers in a circle. Within the following week, on a date chosen by the syndicate, the aeroplane must repeat the performance. The Wrights were to receive $20,000 after the accomplishment of these flights, and if within the four months following, another aviator succeeded in equaling or beating this performance, the contract would be void.

With this important document in mind, Wilbur elected to visit France again, and use the 1907 *Flyer* still stored at Le Havre, while Orville would stay at home and handle the newly arranged demonstrations for the United States War Department with a brand-new machine. Neither brother had flown for two years, so they both returned to Kitty Hawk and spent several weeks in intensive practice on their old 1905 biplane.

When Wilbur arrived in France he set up the machine at the Le Mans factory of Léon Bollée, one of France's leading automobile manufacturers, and from there made a number of flights that eventually toppled every European record.

Wilbur worked at Bollée's from six o'clock in the morning until nightfall, sharing his midday lunch with the factory hands. He took so much time assembling the machine that the French press and public lost interest in him. His passionate attention to detail and his insistence on doing everything himself made him the butt of their latest jokes, and one of the newspapers called the taciturn American a charlatan.

But he had some excuse for the delay, for the boxes containing the aeroplane had been carelessly opened by the customs men, and more carelessly closed again. Ten or so wing ribs were broken, and much of the fabric surface damaged. Aluminum parts had been bent, the radiators were "badly mashed," as Wilbur put it, the seat broken, and the magneto seriously damaged. "I suspect the axle is bent a little, the tubes of the screw supports are also mashed and bent and all the bolts and nuts necessary for proper assembly seem to be scattered all over the place—or lost."

However, Wilbur judged the new *Flyer* ready for a test flight by August 8. The Jockey Club of France had given him permission to use the Hunaudières racecourse, a few miles from Le Mans, as an airfield, and there he erected a wooden hangar and a new catapult-derrick and launching rail. The Wrights still used the skid and trolley system for taking off and landing.

Success Before the Skeptics

The great day fell on a Saturday, and when a rumor was passed that the American would try a test flight, hundreds of visitors arrived at the racecourse, many of them skeptical that this reserved American would ever fly, for they had read the recent newspaper accounts, and had heard what seemed like mythical reports of what the Wrights had accomplished—or were supposed to have achieved on the other side of the Atlantic. They could not stay away from the Hunaudières racecourse.

Before Wilbur started his engine for the historic flight, an argument broke out when French press photographers who had been waiting about more than a week, prepared to take pictures of the take-off and flight, but the airman from America explained that the exclusive rights to photographs of the first flight in France had been sold to a New York agency. Wilbur steadfastly stood his ground, saying he would not fly until the French photographers gave their word of honor not to take pictures while the machine was in the air. They agreed reluctantly, and nodding to several members of the French Aero Club, Wilbur said, "Gentlemen, I'm going to fly." He started his engine, took his place in the pilot's seat and pulled the catapult-release cable. The *Flyer* glided along the launching rail and rose gracefully into the air. Swishing along at 30 feet altitude, Wilbur raced over the pattern of upturned faces, flew two effortless circuits of the racecourse, and wheeled in a tight figure-8 over the grandstand before touching down for a perfect landing.

"It was like a partridge returning to its nest!" one astonished Frenchman exclaimed.

Actually, this flight was only 107 seconds in duration, but nothing like it had been seen in France. All previous skepticism and ridicule were forgotten as the crowd surged forward to congratulate the American aeronaut. Wilbur literally was overwhelmed with their generous praise. The famed Louis Blériot said to one reporter, "For us in France and everywhere, a new era in mechanical flight has begun. I am not sufficiently calm after the event thoroughly to express my opinion. My view can best be expressed in these words—it is marvelous!"

Wilbur Wright became a hero overnight. The public was captivated by his quiet manner and total lack of conceit. He was induced to remain at the Hunaudières racecourse for another two weeks during which time he made nine flights in all. With deliberate singleness of purpose he concentrated on improving his flying technique, increasing each flight's duration until he made one flight lasting 8 minutes, 13 seconds. But the racecourse had a fringe of tall elms which presented obvious dangers for extended flying, and taking advantage of a break in the weather Wilbur moved to the artillery range at Camp d'Auvours eight miles outside Le Mans. There on a truckle bed he slept near his machine, disdaining many invitations to accept free hotel accommodations and more convenient dining facilities.

Still flying in a simple business suit, golf cap, a high starched collar and tie above a bilious green shirt, Wilbur gave his first exhibition at the new field early in September. He skimmed into the air and stayed aloft for 19 minutes, 48 seconds, covering a distance of 16½ miles. Once more the onlookers mobbed Wilbur who just smiled his appreciation, saying very little. While he was engaged with a number of well-known personalities who had turned up to witness his exhibition, a French photographer crept in and began to take close-up pictures of the Wright biplane. Wilbur and two gendarmes immediately gave chase—which was the general idea—leaving the field open to the rest of the newspapermen to move in and shoot all the photographs they desired. The next day every cinema house in Paris was advertising a showing of authentic films of this new, record-breaking flight. The previous word-of-honor arrangement had been conveniently forgotten.

After that experience Wilbur made a snide remark about the efforts of European aviators. He said, "My contract here in France stipulates that I should fly, not hop from the ground, or flutter along like a hen chased by a dog." The remark was uncalled for, but it was pertinent. Wilbur Wright was capable of long, maneuverable flights in which his machine was under complete control at all times. In fact, his displays were so fascinating it became fashionable to take the train from Paris to Le Mans, and then drive out to Camp d'Avours to watch these exhibitions. Even Margherita, Dowager Queen of Italy, turned up, and remarked, "You have let me witness the most astonishing spectacle I have ever seen."

Despite his natural reticence, Wilbur was the perfect showman. On occasions he would cut his engine when at good altitude, and the crowd would fully expect to see the American biplane plunge out of control from the sky above. During one of these tricks, Miss Pierpont Morgan was so overcome with fear she fainted dead away, but came to just in time to see Wilbur make a series of perfect glides, swoops, and then with his engine still just ticking over, vol-plane down to a faultless landing. Two Russian officers also witnessed most of these exhibitions.

Conversely, while all of Europe's men of science and women of fashion were paying homage to this quiet Ameri-can, France's foremost aviator, Henri Farman, was in the United States attempting to give a comparable exhibition. A group of St. Louis businessmen had invited Farman to tour New York, Chicago, and Philadelphia with his Voisin biplane. A complete publicity campaign was inaugurated, but in the United States Farman was accorded much the same treatment as had been given the Wrights. The Ameri-can public was apathetic to heavier-than-air flying.

Farman did make fifteen flights from Long Island's Brighton Beach racetrack despite unfavorable weather. Most of these efforts were of short duration, and the ex-pected crowds stayed at home. The whole tour was a finan-cial failure, and Farman's backers went into liquidation. The Voisin was impounded for debts, and Henri returned to France a keenly disappointed man.

The Death of Lieutenant Selfridge

While Wilbur was striving to lengthen the duration of every flight in France, and working hard to meet the terms of the Lazare-Weiller syndicate contract, the limelight flashed back to Orville who had remained at home to carry out the military trials' stipulations at Fort Myer, Virginia. Orville made his first official government flight on September 3, 1908. Some records claim that this effort was made on September 4, but at any rate he took off from a very limited area, and circling the field, stayed in the air for about four minutes. The exhibition amazed the small crowd on hand, and hard-boiled newspapermen were seen to stare, almost refusing to believe their eyes. Everyone felt he had just witnessed the "impossible."

On September 10, Orville gave a second exhibition, and remained in the air for one hour, five minutes. On that same day Lieutenant Frank P. Lahm, later a brigadier general in the U. S. Air Corps, was taken aloft, but he was not the Wrights' first passenger. Orville had taken up his mechanic, Charley Furnas, on May 14, 1908, as an experiment before undertaking an official passenger flight. The second "official" passenger was Major George O. Squier, Acting Chief Signal Officer of the U. S. Army, who went aloft with Orville on September 12, making a flight of nine minutes. Later that day the Dayton pilot set a new endurance record of one hour, fourteen minutes at an altitude of 250 feet. With this exhibition, in which military men were enjoying front-row seats, everyone was certain that the aeroplane would become an important factor in warfare, but not one uniformed official at Fort Myer would have dared predict that within six years aircraft would have an important role in World War I's First Battle of the Marne (September 9, 1914).

But the world's first aeroplane tragedy occurred at the height of this success. At his own request Lieutenant Thomas E. Selfridge of the U. S. Army was taken aloft as an official observer on September 17, 1908. This was the same Lieutenant Selfridge who had been a member of Professor Bell's Aerial Experiment Association, and who had designed the association's *Red Wing* biplane.

From all accounts, because of Selfridge's association with Glenn Curtiss, Orville was reluctant, but decided to make this flight one that would impress the young officer, especially as he was an official Army observer. This is not to imply that the Dayton man made a show-off display; on the contrary he flew his biplane with conservative skill through simple circuits. After a beautiful take-off, Orville put the machine through three perfect circuits of the Fort Myer area, and was starting a fourth at an altitude of around 250 feet when a light tapping, or vibration, was heard at the rear of the machine. The pilot thought it was coming from the chain drive, but when he glanced back he could see nothing out of the ordinary. He decided, however, to shut off the engine, and make an immediate landing. He had hardly moved the controls to carry out this decision when two sharp thumps shook the machine violently, and the biplane swerved sharply to the right, indicating that something very serious was wrong. Orville then cut the engine completely, and saw that he was heading straight into a gully filled with small trees.

Instead of risking a landing there, he tried to turn to the left and get down on the parade ground. By that time the controls of the tail assembly were inoperative, so he worked on the wing-warping gear, hoping to level the machine out and fly straight on. At that point the machine suddenly nosed down, and for about 50 feet seemed to be heading for a nose-on crash, although Orville had the elevator turned up to its limit. When the machine was about 25 feet from the ground, it began to right itself, and had there been another 20 or 30 feet to spare, they might have landed safely. But there was not enough height to make a complete recovery. The biplane hit with such impact that Lieutenant Selfridge was fatally injured, dying a few hours later. An examination disclosed that his skull had been fractured when he hit against one of the struts. Though believed to be fatally hurt at first, Orville escaped with a fractured leg and four broken ribs. Up to now no one had considered the use of safety belts.

The day after the Fort Myer accident, the mechanics, Taylor and Furnas, brought the broken propeller and some of the other damaged parts to the hospital where Orville was recuperating. After a cursory examination, and a later inspection, he determined the cause of the accident. Just before the flight a new pair of propellers, several inches longer than any used previously, had been bolted on, and shortly after the engine was started, a longitudinal crack developed in one blade of the right-hand propeller. The crack widened and the blade flattened, losing much of its thrust so that the thrusts of the two blades became unequal setting up a severe vibration that affected the propeller shaft housing. This vibration then loosened one of the stay wires that held in position the tube in which the propeller shaft turned. This allowed the propeller to swing sideways and twist forward until one blade hit and tore loose a guy wire supporting the vertical tail. This permitted the tail assembly to assume a nearly horizontal position, and pressure on the tail's underside raised the rear section of the plane, causing it to make its tragic nosedive toward the ground.

In France, Wilbur was desolate over the accident and Lieutenant Selfridge's death. He called off for the time being his entry in the Michelin & Commission de Aviation prize events, but he was well pleased with the efforts his brother had made at Fort Myer, and wrote that his flights had revolutionized the world's beliefs "regarding the practicability of flight."

Once he was satisfied that Orville was not hurt too seriously and was getting good attention in a military hospital, Wilbur renewed his assaults on his previous records. On September 28 he won the Commission of Aviation's 5000-franc prize by making twenty-four circuits of two poles set one kilometer apart, covering a distance of 48 kilometers in one hour, seven minutes. Part of this money he sent home to Dayton, and some he spent to overhaul the engine that was using oil at a very fast rate. By this time, too, the supremacy of the Wright biplane was no longer questioned in France. The Aero Club voted the Dayton brothers a gold medal. All their newspaper and aviation critics had been won over, and to top all his efforts, Wilbur took Léon Bollée, who weighed 240 pounds, on a flight, circling the artillery field several times, and astonishing most of the experts who viewed the spectacle. He also took Paul Painlevé, vice-president of the commission and a member of the French Aviation Institute, aloft for a flight that lasted one hour, ten minutes. Painlevé had wished to make a flight as he was expected to present a paper to be read before the Institute.

When Wilbur had completed all requirements of the Lazare-Weiller contract, the syndicate announced plans to manufacture fifty Wright machines in Europe, but the bankers concerned demanded that Wilbur agree to train three volunteers as pilots and Count de Lambert, Captain Lucas de Girardville, and Paul Tissandier were named for this instruction. With all this publicity several European governments showed renewed interest in the Wright machine, and many military attachés visited Camp d'Avours to watch the flying exhibitions, but no British military man turned up. About this time, however, Lord Northcliffe of the *Daily Mail* offered a prize of $2500 for a flight across the English Channel, and added privately that he would give Wilbur $7500 extra, or $10,000 in all, if he would make an attempt for the prize and win it. Wilbur was undecided what course to take although the prize money would be welcome; he felt he was involved in too many important business features to take the time. But by early November Wilbur said that if the weather would hold he would be willing to risk the cross-Channel flight. He realized that such a feat would greatly impress the governments of France, Germany, and Great Britain. Unfortunately, he was never able to make the attempt, and the honor went to Louis Blériot the following summer—July 5, 1909.

British Interest

Though the British government may have seemed apathetic, there were many young Britishers who displayed intense personal interest in the American aeronaut's exhibitions, among whom was the Honorable Charles Stewart Rolls, motorcar manufacturer, and sportsman aeronaut who had completed one hundred lighter-than-air ascents, and who was to become one of Britain's most beloved airmen. Charles Rolls managed to get on the airfield and gain an introduction to Wilbur who, on learning of the Englishman's aeronautical background, turned to him with a pleasant smile and said, "Mr. Rolls, I think I'll take you up this morning."

From that day on Charles Rolls was a confirmed heavier-than-air enthusiast, and promptly took an option on the first of the Wright machines to be built in France. He made the first cross-Channel flight from England to France in it, and was the first man to make a nonstop round-trip flight of the famous body of water. Charles Rolls was tragically killed while competing in a spot-landing event at Bournemouth on July 12, 1910.

Other Britons who flew with Wilbur were Major B. F. S. Baden-Powell, brother of the founder of the Boy Scouts, Frank Hedges Butler, Aero Club member and all-round sportsman, and Griffith Brewer who became the Wrights' most important friend in Great Britain.

Another British pilgrim who made his way to Le Mans was a plodding unknown who had been attempting for months to build an aeroplane at the Brooklands race track. He was A. V. Roe, who when his money ran out was ejected from the automobile speed center, and had to set up a shop in a disused railroad arch on the desolate Lea marshes. Although he was nearly at the end of his resources, he was determined to meet Wilbur Wright and to watch him fly, so he rode his bicycle to Southampton, sailed steerage for Saint-Malo, and pedaled the remaining hundred miles to Le Mans. Hearing of his story, Wilbur gave generously of his time and advice to the man who was to become one of Great Britain's aircraft manufacturers.

There were more dinners and honors for the Wrights. The French government wanted to bestow the Legion of Honor on Wilbur, but he declined, saying that it was impossible for him to accept any honor that Orville could not share, so eventually the honor was awarded to both brothers. The Aero Club of Great Britain also voted a gold medal which was bestowed on both Wilbur and Orville. Attractive business offers rapidly followed; an Italian firm offered them 500,000 francs and 25 per cent of the profits for the right to manufacture Wright biplanes in that country. Wilbur next agreed to build ten machines for Russia for the sum of $100,000, and then construct additional machines for a royalty of $2500 apiece. The aforementioned French company was incorporated with a fund of 800,000 francs of which the Wrights were to be given 250,000 francs. Later details disclose that the company was to be headed by a son of Premier Georges Clemenceau, and it was to guarantee to sell twenty-five machines a year with a major portion of the income going to the Wrights. As to their American business, the brothers hoped to draw the promised $25,000 for the first machine delivered to the United States Army, and then sell the government additional machines for $7500 apiece.

Another Flying School

To fulfill the obligation to train three pilots, the Wrights arranged to take over some ground outside Pau in the winter resort area of France. There the town built them a house for living quarters and room for shop work. A local hotel agreed to furnish first-class accommodations for Wilbur, Orville, and their sister Katherine, who had been induced to take a year's leave of absence from schoolteaching and act as their social secretary and general domestic manager. Shortly thereafter the Aeronautical Society of Rome invited them to Italy for a month, and offered $10,000 for a biplane and the training of an Italian pilot.

Before making the move to Pau, Wilbur made his final try for the Michelin prize, worth $4000, on December 31, 1908. He remained in the air for 2 hours, 20 minutes, covering a distance of 124 kilometers, or about 90 miles, in a drizzle of sleet and rain. There were no other competitors for this prize, so the money was handed to Wilbur along with the gold trophy which was given into the care of the Aero Club of the Sarthe of which Wilbur was a member.

The contract to train three pilots was begun at Le Mans, but was moved to Pau when the winter weather set in. Orville, who was now fully recovered, took over some of the instruction. Count de Lambert and Tissandier proved to be excellent pilots, but Lieutenant Calderara, the Italian student, was prone to accidents. "He was a cigarette fiend," Wilbur grumbled. "What else could we expect?"

Orville also handled the business administration, and sent their brother Lorin two drafts on New York banks, for $5797 and $21,297.19 which he suggested Lorin deposit in building associations at 4 per cent. Both brothers were interested in real-estate investments. By coincidence J. P. Morgan, his sister and daughter visited the Rome camp two weeks later.

Before the Pau and Rome obligations were finished, the Wrights signed a contract with the Short brothers of England, who were fitting out a flying field on the Isle of Sheppey at the mouth of the Thames, whereby they were to build Wright machines on a royalty basis. They had opportunities to close out their business in England and leave it in the hands of the Short brothers, but decided to hold onto it for the present.

In early May of 1909 the Wrights were back in Dayton preparing to build a new biplane to continue the Fort Myer tests. Much time was wasted in traveling between Dayton and Washington to receive medals and citations—even the city of Dayton finally had a "home coming" that lasted two days—and it was June 28, 1909, before Orville could start the new series of flights. However, by July 30 all requirements had been fulfilled, and on that final day, carrying

Lieutenant Benjamin D. Foulois as a passenger, Orville made the first cross-country flight to Alexandria and return, a distance of ten miles, risking the fact that there was no suitable place to land if trouble should force them down.

For these tests the Wrights received their $25,000, plus an additional $5000, or 10 per cent for each mile at speeds above 40 miles per hour.

As soon as this contract was signed, Orville and Katherine traveled to Germany where Orville had agreed to train two fliers for the German Wright company. They were accommodated in Berlin at the Esplande Hotel, gratis. Despite his serious accident, Orville loved to fly, whereas Wilbur, after his first few flights, preferred to stay on the ground; he flew solely for business reasons. Although the Wrights made remarkable records of time and distance, neither pilot achieved much in the matter of altitude. Wilbur seldom flew above a hundred feet, but Orville, who was more daring, raised the world's altitude record from 100 to 172 meters—above 500 feet—on September 16, 1909, in Germany. To match this, Wilbur, back in the States, made a historic flight from Governors Island in New York harbor, up the Hudson River to Grant's Tomb, and back again. Because of the risk of a possible landing on the water, Wilbur roped a canoe to the under section of the plane in the hope the canoe might act as a pontoon to keep the machine afloat.

After this exhibition Wilbur next went to College Park, Maryland, to train two U. S. Army Signal Corps officers as pilots. They were Frank P. Lahm and Frederick E. Humphreys. Their course began on October 8 and concluded October 28. Later, Wilbur also gave lessons to Lieutenant Benjamin D. Foulois.

It will be seen that by the autumn of 1909 the Wrights had captured every record in Europe and the United States.

They had built up several business associations that promised remarkable profits. They had the most efficient heavier-than-air machine in the world, fully covered by patents, and, equally important, they had won acclaim, honors, decorations, and rewards for their work. Now both men felt they could retire from active flying and devote their time to further research and improvement of their invention.

But progress elsewhere forbade such an Arcadian future. There was considerable trouble ahead, most of it in the cocking main of business. They were years proving their exclusive right to the wing-warping device that furnished lateral control, years that took a great deal from the two brothers. Experimenters everywhere were poring over their designs, and photographs were taken and published by newspapers in order to usurp the Wrights' varied inventions. These business and legal battles occurred all over America and Europe, and in the United States the controversies were costly in time and funds. Could they have put their business problems into reliable hands, they might have spent more time on further development of their invention, but there was little opportunity for them to take a broad view of the new science. They persisted in continuing with their primary biplane design. They held to the dual-propeller propulsion system with its chain drive that permitted but a limited progress in power delivery. They continued with the forward elevator assembly and their wing-warping devices instead of delving into improvements on the hinged aileron, the only wing control that could keep pace with the increased speeds that were to be required in military and commercial aviation. Apparently they ignored the tractor monoplane, despite the success Louis Blériot had had with his machines. They never considered placing the pilot and passenger in an enclosed cockpit, nor did they accept the fact that aircraft speeds would ever reach anything like a hundred miles an hour. Right into the middle of World War I Orville had no concept of the pace military aviation was making or any general understanding of the tactical problems involved in aerial warfare. Well into 1917 Orville still believed that the aeroplane was fitted only for military scouting, and only in rare instances did he conceive the value of aerial bombing. Wilbur, who died of typhoid fever in 1912, never saw any of the Great War's employment of the machine they had invented.

All through the early 1900s the Wrights fully realized what they had produced, but they had no idea that the financial future of the Wright dynasty lay in the development of aircraft engines rather than in the production and design of aircraft that would fulfill future requirements. Still, there was glory enough in what they had accomplished. They had given man the secret of mechanized flight.

CHAPTER VI

The New Industry

The Wright Racer • The Aeronautic Society of New York • Kimball's Helicopter • Fred Shneider's Bad Luck • Another Curtiss Case • But Accidents Will Happen • The Loss of Delagrange • The Fate of Georges Chavez • Ralph Johnstone Joins the List

---

Until early 1908 the guidance and responsibility of heavier-than-air advance appeared to be in the hands of the Wright brothers, Glenn Curtiss, and a small circle of European sportsmen who had both the spirit and finances to engage in this daring science, but by 1909 there were forty licensed aviators in the world, all contributing their efforts and thoughts to its progress. In fact, the aeroplane had become not only a force that was to change the course of civilization, but it was hatching a brand-new industry.

The Wrights had sold manufacturing rights for their biplane to several European combines, and had signed additional contracts with their own government. In fact, for a year or so they seemed to have the full potential of the aeroplane completely in their own hands. How their business hopes reached fruition makes interesting reading.

Once the Wright machine had been accepted abroad and at home, commercial interests in the United States saw the possibilities in the Wright patents, and several American financiers made proposals to form an aeroplane company, but none of these reached a satisfactory conclusion. In fact, the first American company organized to manufacture the Wright machine was formed by Clinton R. Peterkin, a young man only twenty-four years old.

Clinton Peterkin had worked in the office of J. P. Morgan & Company from the age of fifteen, and after a few years in which he made the most of his opportunities, he saw how new business enterprises were conceived and put into operation. On hearing that Wilbur Wright would be spending a few days in New York, young Peterkin called on him at his hotel, and laid out his ideas. Wilbur was kind and understanding, but explained that he would prefer a company in which men of financial stature and business consequence would be included. When Peterkin explained that he "had worked for Mr. J. P. Morgan," Wilbur smiled and told him to go ahead and see what progress could be made.

Playing into this Horatio Alger story, Mr. Morgan showed immediate interest, and assured Peterkin he would buy stock, adding that he would induce his friend Judge Elbert H. Gary, head of the United States Steel Corporation, to consider such a project. Next, a distant relative of Peterkin, De Lancey Nicoll, a senior partner in a law firm, learning what the young man was promoting, offered his assistance, and in a short time an impressive list of influential men had enrolled in his proposed company. Among them were Cornelius Vanderbilt, August Belmont, Howard Gould, Theodore P. Shonts, Allan A. Ryan, Morton F.

Plant, and Andrew Freedman. Realizing that their efforts were coming to a business head, the Wrights explained that they wished to include their friends Robert J. Collier, publisher of *Collier's Weekly*, and Frederick M. Alger of Detroit. By this time most of the subscribers felt that Mr. Morgan and Judge Gary would dominate the company, so they were offhandedly advised that the stock was oversubscribed. Mr. Morgan sensed the situation and promptly withdrew his offer to take stock, and also eliminated Judge Gary.

Less than a month after Peterkin had first talked with Wilbur, the Wright Company was incorporated on November 22, 1909, with a capital stock of $200,000. The Wright brothers received stock and cash for all rights to their patents in the United States, and a royalty of 10 per cent on all planes sold. The Wright Company thenceforward would bear the expense of prosecuting all suits against patent infringements.

The company first opened an administrative office at 527 Fifth Avenue, New York, but its factory was to be erected in Dayton, starting about January 1910. In the beginning the company rented floor space in another factory building, but started to build a modern plant that was ready for occupancy in November 1910. Here hurriedly recruited workmen were soon producing two aeroplanes a month.

As soon as machines and pilots were available, plans were made to attract some financial returns from public exhibitions, and Roy Knabenshue, a Toledo aeronaut who had been making balloon flights since his early teens, was called in to handle this outside project. Knabenshue was most adept at promotional work and soon had a number of Wright pilots performing all over the country.

By 1910 the Dayton team finally had accepted the wheeled undercarriage and discarded their catapult take-off device to which they had clung since 1905. Whether they themselves had adopted bicycle wheels, or European manufacturers of their machines had used wheeled landing gears to compete with other makes, is not clear, but by 1910 the Wrights were finally meeting the competition.

This year also saw changes in the control system, though they still retained their original wing-warping feature. In their 1910 models they had devised a control in which the horizontal rudder was interlocked with the control that worked the wing-warping feature. In other words, the rudder and aileron effect were linked for a combined action. By this time, too, the brothers had worked out a design that eliminated the forward assembly carrying the elevator rudder, a change that considerably improved the over-all appearance of the machine. This was dubbed the "headless" Wright, and on its being displayed at the Asbury Park, New Jersey, meet that year it was disclosed that the control for horizontal flight was now carried on the tail assembly behind the directional rudder.

The Wright Racer

At this time, too, probably to compete in the many aviation meets in which speed was a prime factor, the Wrights produced what was known generally as the Wright *Racer*, Model R, a diminutive version of previous models. Originally, it was built for competition in the Gordon Bennett Cup race at Belmont Park, New York, but due to a last-minute accident it could not take part. The Model R had a wing-span of 26½ feet, an over-all length of 24 feet, and its height from the ground to the top plane was only 6 feet, 10 inches. The interesting feature of the Wright *Racer* was its 8-cylinder V-type engine that produced between 50 and 60 horsepower. Twin propellers were turned through the standard sprocket-and-gear system. There was space for only a pilot, and aboard one of these models Ralph Johnstone set a new altitude record of 9714 feet, but as for speed, the *Racer* attained only 41 miles per hour. At best it could be considered little more than a "flyabout" for the sporting trade.

Meanwhile, in order to fill a number of contracts in the United States, the Wright designers continually modified and improved their Model B, or "headless," machine until 1914, but they did not adopt the enclosed fuselage until 1915 when World War I had been in progress for twelve months. In fact, this model saw the end of their aircraft development as the Wright Company. Because of their hidebound determination to stick to the biplane pusher type they never were able to compete in the military field. True, a few Model B planes were employed at United States Army training schools, but by 1914 all pusher types were condemned as the result of many fatalities that occurred at the training schools.

This decision left the Army with only five machines suitable for instruction (Thomas-Morse tractors), and at this point Glenn Curtiss, who had been developing a tractor biplane with the engine in the front, took over much of the American aviation industry. This early model was improved and developed into the famous JN-I, the first of a series of trainers that were to become known to a whole generation of student pilots as the "Jenny."

During the war the Dayton-Wright Airplane Company was organized at Dayton with Charles F. Kettering as presi-

dent. This company which was formed for quantity production of aeroplanes to government specifications, turned out
a number of DH-4A biplanes, and a small number of civilian types, called *Honeymoon Express*, a peacetime version of the World War I bomber with a waterproof canopy
fitted over the rear seat. The organization also produced
a single-seater known as the Dayton-Wright *Messenger*,
powered with a 2-cylinder, 4-cycle De Palma engine giving
out 37 horsepower. This little machine, however, was never
put into production.

In 1916 the surviving brother, Orville, merged his original Wright Company with the Glenn L. Martin Company,
the Simplex Automobile Company, and the General Aeronautic Company of America, thus forming the Wright-Mar-
tin Aircraft Corporation which concentrated on the production of Hispano Suiza engines, and some aircraft of
official government design. Orville had little to do with any
of this, but continued to work as a private experimenter at
his factory in Dayton.

Although years behind their European contemporaries,
the Curtiss company became the leading aeronautical firm
in the United States, but it never built anything but a third-
rate trainer all through the critical years of World War I.
Military aviation was years in attracting the imagination
of America. Safe from attack behind its ocean barriers, she
lacked the intense spirit of international competition that
inspired the military establishments of the European pow-
ers prior to the Great War. In addition to the lack of money
and defense requirements, there was the problem of training and keeping pilots. Although willing to patronize the
Roman-holiday pattern of exhibition, Americans were quick
to appreciate the dangers of flying, and the high fatality
rate of aviation training. Twelve of the first forty-eight of-

ficers detailed for flight training were killed, and the War Department became more and more reluctant to assign officers from other services to assume flying duties. Many of those interviewed complained that they saw no future in the aviation service.

All this had its effect on aircraft design, development, and manufacturing as no American businessman could foresee substantial contracts for great numbers of aircraft designed only for military operations. Instead, they had to rely on public exhibitions, the training of civilian pilots, and the prize money that came from these country-fair sideshows.

The Aeronautic Society of New York

But this is not to suggest that the United States lacked scientific interest in heavier-than-air flying, or that there was a dearth of substantial curiosity in the science, or men who were willing to risk their lives in the development of powered aircraft. The history of the Aeronautic Society of New York between July 1908 and December 1909 gives an indication of the intense interest shown by a small but doughty band of scientific pioneers.

It was the first organization in the United States formed for the practical pursuit of the problem of mechanical flight by man. It possibly was the first such organization in the world to have its own flying grounds, and to provide workshops, sheds, and tools for its members. It certainly was among the first to furnish its experimenters with suitable engines with which to power their machines. To all intents and purposes, the Aeronautic Society of New York was the first society in the world to look around among the young

experimenters in the country, and to give one of the most
promising, Glenn H. Curtiss, a commission to build a flying
machine. It not only gave the commission at Curtiss's own
price, but also paid him a large sum of money to help him
start on the work. The result of this was that in open competition the United States was able to win the leading aviation laurel of the year—the Gordon Bennett Trophy—at
Reims, France, on August 22, 1909, defeating crack pilots
from Great Britain, Germany, and France.

This unusual association was founded on June 10, 1908,
when about fifty enthusiasts attended the organization
meeting. Bylaws were drawn up, and arrangements made
to lease the old race track at Morris Park, New York City,
that at the time included 137 acres and was but a short
walk from Bronx Park. Trolley cars ran all the way up to
the race track, bearing patrons from the center of the city
within forty minutes. Nearby were a fashionable hotel,
several good restaurants, and a number of first-class room-
ing houses.

One of the first events of the society's program was an
exhibition, and Léon Delagrange of France, who had just
made a sensational flight of fifteen minutes, was invited
to bring his machine across the Atlantic and show the members of the association what heavier-than-air flying was like.
The Wrights, of course, were too busy in Europe, or were
fulfilling U.S. government contracts. Unquestionably, Delagrange should have drawn great crowds to Morris Park,
and the Aeronautic Society of New York might have filled
its coffers with much-needed money to finance other features of its program.

But the arrangements for the Delagrange exhibition
leaked out, and a rival syndicate in St. Louis was quickly
formed to bring over Henri Farman who also was consid-

ered to be a big drawing card for such affairs. The result was that neither organization had the expected success, and the rival syndicate wound up deeply in debt. This was typical of many aviation exhibitions, contests, and meets of this period. Farman was to some extent disgraced and his Voisin aeroplane held for the syndicate's debts. This failure was due somewhat to the Frenchman's refusal to fly higher than 300 feet. To the American patrons this was hardly flying—or only just. They experienced no particular thrill in seeing a man swish past a grandstand only a few dozen feet off the ground. They had been nurtured on balloon ascensions and daring parachute descents from great heights, so the spectacle of a comical aeroplane chugging past at what seemed to be a very cautious altitude soon became boring, and the expected crowds stayed home in large numbers.

The Aeronautic Society was fully organized and incorporated by July 1908, and the officers pro tem. appointed. They were Lee S. Burridge, president, and Louis R. Adams, Stanley Y. Beach, William J. Hammer, Ernest L. Jones, Wilbur R. Kimball, Henry H. Law, Orrel A. Parker, L. G. W. Schroeder, A. Leo Stevens, A. C. Triaca, and Roger B. Whitman as directors. L. G. W. Schroeder was secretary.

Right from the beginning meetings were held and lectures given in the society's big room located in the old race track building, and as soon as workshops were available in what had been stables, neighbors in the area noted a number of queer-looking machines chugging up and down the race track. On weekends small knots of people would appear at breaks in the ancient fencing to stare at the strange operations. But this initial interest soon waned because the onlookers had expected to see flying machines darting about in all directions and at all levels. When these anticipated marvels failed to materialize, they lost interest and applied jests and ridicule to what they had observed.

A great deal of this was to be expected as the members of the Aeronautic Society were at first carried away by their own enthusiasm. Releases to newspapers attracted a number of reporters, but when no flying was on schedule what was accomplished was seldom recorded. Also, a few members believed that all they needed to get into the air was to build some sort of winged machine, powered with an engine that turned some form of propeller. What they expected to do once they had left the ground, was not fully explained. They were long on theory, calculations, and physical activity, but they had not delved deeply into the personal equation.

Kimball's Helicopter

The first machine to be completed was a helicopter built by Wilbur R. Kimball. It was an intricate piece of machinery in which twenty propellers were driven by an engine designed by George J. Altham. This was a 4-cylinder, 2-cycle plant that developed 50 horsepower at 2000 revolutions per minute. With its cooling system and fuel, the Altham engine weighed only 180 pounds, and though it could be run for long periods at high speed, it was not capable of handling the very intricate transmission system required to drive Kimball's twenty propellers. Consequently, after many months of work with this weird machine, the inventor put it aside to await another engine.

The next machine produced by the Aeronautic Society was a glider, designed by C. J. Hendrickson, that to some degree foreshadowed the famous *Demoiselle* built by Santos-Dumont—a lightweight monoplane weighing only 330 pounds and still to be seen in the Aeronautical Museum at Chalis-Meudon near Paris. What success Hendrickson had with his craft has not been explained.

Lawrence J. Lesh, not a member at the time, also built a glider that he flew by being towed by a motorboat, by a horse, and even by an automobile. Only seventeen years old, Lesh had done a great deal of experimental gliding, and had made an attempt to win the *Brooklyn Eagle* gold medal at Morris Park, but after being towed to a sufficient height, he was hampered by an unruly crowd and broke an ankle on landing.

A powered machine was also built by C. W. Williams who had new theories on wing construction. This was a squarish monoplane in which the wing fabric was seemingly laced to the main spars. This was typical of the time for in many instances these early designers just built wing frames and then had someone else make sleeve-type coverings that were held in position by tapes or grommets. There was no such item as a taut, lacquered wing covering. Although William's freakish biplane was ready soon after the society was formed, he had no power plant because Kimball was still using the Altham engine.

On the Election Day that William Howard Taft was voted into the White House, November 3, 1908, the society staged a general exhibition to show the public what it had accomplished so far. It was planned to display some machines in the course of construction or development—gliders, helicopters, and other aerial apparatus. More than 20,000 eager patrons gathered, and at times the crowd was unmanageable. They saw Kimball's helicopter set out on the line, C. W. Williams's monoplane fitted with a 7-horsepower engine to show how the propeller was turned, and a gigantic Beach-Whitehead biplane, powered with two tractor propellers run off an engine mounted below a boatlike body, but the machinery, pulleys, belts, and brackets to carry all this appeared more suitable for a steam roller than an aeroplane. This display ended the society's outdoor program for 1908, and during the following winter all business was transacted at the Automobile Club of America's facilities in New York City.

Fred Shneider's Bad Luck

While most activity of the society had drifted back to the city, Fred Shneider had been building a biplane, weighing 450 pounds, that was to be powered by an air-cooled rotary engine turning three aluminum propellers of variable pitch. This was a new twist in power output, and a number of press representatives were on hand to record its first flight.

Shneider had built a typical biplane with ailerons set between the outer interplane struts, and a normal tail assembly. He had protected the pilot's seat with a conical nacelle that gave it a somewhat racy appearance. Unfortunately, the rotary engine was unfitted for the work involved and the experiment was a failure. Later, Shneider modified this machine, used but two propellers, disposed of the wheeled gear, introduced a set of skids, and planned to take off by catapult.

Again, this determined man made a public trial, and this time the engine ran well. The catapult gear sent the machine forward and Shneider landed about 170 yards from the end of the monorail. Whether he actually flew that distance was an open question, but some witnesses declared that the machine was airborne some of the time. The landing was made with no trouble or damage.

In a third version of this biplane Shneider replaced the rotary engine with another furnished by the society. This power plant was four times heavier, and he got away cleanly from the catapult and rose into the air, but the instant the craft was free of the ground the wings collapsed. The light plane was not stressed for this heavy engine, or the speed with which it forced the machine through the air. Shneider was not injured, but his invention was a complete wreck. However, within a week Shneider started to build a fourth aircraft.

Another Curtiss Case

During the winter of 1908–09 the Aeronautic Society took a step that was to have a far-reaching effect on American aviation, one that played a big role in the competition to stage the first great International Aviation Meeting that was to be held at Belmont Park in 1910. After some careful consideration it was decided that the society as a body should do something to create a more general interest in the development of mechanical flight. It was agreed to give a commission to someone who actually had made flights, and could guarantee by past performances to build a machine that would fly at the society's summer exhibition.

At this time Glenn Curtiss had had a large part in building four machines, all of which had flown. The most recent was the *June Bug* of Curtiss's own designing. He was therefore selected on January 21, 1909; a contract was drawn and $500 given him on signing. All told he was to receive $5000 for a machine, and at Curtiss's request the existence of the contract was to be kept secret until he had severed his connection with Alexander Graham Bell's Aerial Experiment Association. The officials of the society kept their part of the bargain, but by some devious means the facts of the contract leaked out, and the forces in opposition to the society did their utmost to deprive it of the credit for what success was attained.

The details of this affair have been taken from a brochure entitled *An Epitome of the Work of the Aeronautic Society* that was produced by the society's officers, and reprinted in 1958 through the courtesy of the Bausch & Lomb Optical Company.

All through April 1909 preparations were under way for the summer exhibition. The Curtiss machine was due in the first week of May, and the exhibition set for May 22, but on word from Glenn Curtiss asking for an extension of a week, the date was changed to May 29. By now members of the society had a number of experimental machines ready, and a full-scale display was planned. Stanley Y. Beach and Charles F. Willard had a big monoplane of the *Antoinette* type almost finished. Dr. H. W. Walden had virtually completed a tandem biplane. Fred Shneider's third biplane was all but ready, and George A. Lawrence was making rapid headway with his big *Aeriator,* an immense biplane of splendid workmanship. F. B. Rickman was constructing a novel helicopter, and many other members who were building elsewhere agreed to have their machines on hand. All in all there was great promise of the most successful exhibition of its kind ever to be held in the United States.

But ill luck soon took its toll. Curtiss asked for postponement after postponement, and the public came to the conclusion that the exhibit would never take place. Kimball wrecked his machine. A windstorm destroyed the bag of a

semi-dirigible that was to be flown by Carl Myers. When
Glenn Curtiss did arrive he brought a well-constructed
aeroplane that won high praise from all who watched it
being assembled, but for some reason Glenn made no attempts to fly it, or so the committee asserted later.

The exhibition was set finally for Saturday, June 26, 1909,
but it was poorly advertised, and it also suffered from the
general apathy that marked all such displays. During the
previous week Curtiss had promised to make some preliminary flights, and he did actually run up and down the
track in front of the grandstand once or twice, getting his
wheels off the ground, but he risked no true take-offs or
circuits, explaining that the wind was unfavorable. So on
the day of the show the patrons had to be content with looking at experimental machines built by Dr. Greene, the Lawrence brothers, Stanley Y. Beach, F. B. Rickman, and Dr.
Walden. Glenn Curtiss's biplane was also on the line, and finally, when most of the crowd had left, the Hammondsport
pilot took off down the track, rose into the air, made one
turn and landed in front of the grandstand. It was not
much of an effort, but it was the first turn ever made by a
flying machine over New York City. But more important,
the society's exhibition resulted in a very complete set of
rules governing contests of aeroplanes and all kinds of
aerial competitions.

A week later another display was organized by Stanley Y.
Beach, but this too resulted in a serious financial loss. A
few glider flights were attempted, Glenn Curtiss repeated
his one-turn flight of the previous Saturday, and a few motorcycle events were held to round out the program.

Following this halfhearted exhibition, Glenn Curtiss requested permission to move the society's machine to Mineola, Long Island, saying he wished to practice longer flights

over the wide Hempstead plains. Curtiss was granted this favor, and a short while later the society's officials were astonished to learn that he was making these flights under the auspices of the Aero Club of America, an organization that had been associated closely with Curtiss's earlier exploits, though by now the Aeronautic Society had made full payment on the Curtiss biplane. It unquestionably was the property of that organization.

It was during these Mineola practice flights that Glenn Curtiss learned to fly well enough to be nominated by the Aero Club of America to represent the United States at the coming Reims meet. Glenn had barely three weeks in which to build a new biplane, called the *Golden Flyer,* pack it up as his personal baggage with its wings neatly strapped to the fuselage, and hurry across the Atlantic. It was with this aeroplane that he won the Gordon Bennett trophy.

While he was practicing at Mineola, Curtiss taught Alexander Williams and Charles F. Willard to fly the organization's machine, and later on an exhibition corporation, separate from the Aeronautic Society but composed entirely of its members, was formed to lease the Curtiss plane for an exhibition tour that included Toronto, Athens (Pennsylvania), Richmond, Philadelphia, Cincinnati, and Los Angeles. At Cincinnati, Willard flew against Curtiss and won trophies for speed and altitude. At Toronto he flew out over Lake Ontario, and three times suffered embarrassing duckings.

But despite exhibition setbacks and ill luck, the society members continued to turn out some remarkable machines. A noteworthy biplane was constructed by François Raiche and C. M. Crout, one that was patterned after the society's Curtiss machine but presented some improvements, including shock absorbers and brakes on the rear wheels. Short flights were made in it by Crout, and it was one of the featured exhibits at the Aeronautical Exposition held at the old Madison Square Garden, and later at the Danbury (Connecticut) Fair.

Pincus Brauner and A. J. Smith built another biplane that was the second machine made by society members that got off the ground. Dr. H. W. Walden, a New York dentist, built a massive tandem biplane that was to be powered by an engine belonging to the society, but he left his machine out in the open one night and a sudden storm battered the aeroplane to hopeless wreckage before a watchman could save it. Dr. Walden, however, soon had two more models under construction.

R. E. Ernst, another member of the society, made a valiant attempt to add air compression to the available power for flight, in which air was drawn into a hollow chamber by means of fan propellers and allowed to escape through the floor of the chamber. But because a suitable engine was not available at the time, the project had to be abandoned.

The third aircraft to climb into the air under the auspices of the society was Dr. William Greene's biplane. This project had wings that were 40 feet in spread, and after some preliminary flights, Dr. Greene took up two, and then three passengers. The flights of this aeroplane were noteworthy inasmuch as the designer had made use of a stock automobile engine. The power plant was a British-American engine of 26 horsepower that weighed 320 pounds. He later installed a Kimball engine weighing only 160 pounds, and this permitted the doctor to dispense with 70 pounds of ballast that he had hung on the front control to place the center of gravity where it belonged.

It will be seen from the above that the Aeronautic Society of New York made a generous contribution to the science, more than justifying its existence.

But Accidents Will Happen

As in all pioneering projects, accidents and fatalities cluttered the course of the science. Between September 17, 1909, and March 8, 1911, thirty-five fatal accidents occurred, seven of which involved Wright biplanes, and twenty-three biplane types based on the Wrights' original design.

These fatalities were highly featured in the newspapers affording ammunition for the many critics who were loud in their denunciation of all forms of mechanical flight. Yet over this same period 1000 men had taken lessons in flying, most of them completing their tests successfully. In that same space of time ninety people were killed in mountaineering accidents, and, as an aside, fifteen men lost their lives in connection with the construction of the first one hundred miles of railroad lines laid in Great Britain.

In the light of today's standards in aviation, it is interesting to examine the causes of these thirty-five accidents. Breakage of some portion of the machines was noted in eleven instances; in eight accidents it was claimed that the pilots lost control of the machines; four accidents were caused by the aeroplanes being rendered uncontrollable by wind gusts, and as many accidents occurred while the machines were on the ground. Two instances were charged to the illnesses of the pilots while flying, but only one accident was attributed to a faulty engine.

It is easy to account for the fatalities caused by the breakage of some portion of the aircraft, or to the pilots' loss of control. Most of these machines weighed less than a thousand pounds, and they had to be held to this weight so as to stay within the limitations of the engines that seldom were of more than 35 horsepower. Thus, in unfavorable weather these early pilots were pitting their skill and lives aboard a flimsy contrivance, unable to provide the power to offset the force of turbulent winds.

On looking at photographs, drawings, and studying the specifications of these early aircraft, one wonders why these pioneers ever dared to risk any but the most favorable conditions. Then, too, as in other forms of exhibitions before large groups of people, the performers often were inspired to take unjustifiable hazards, to try stunts or maneuvers that were beyond the power or structural limits of their aircraft so as to give the patrons "their money's worth." Many of these pioneering fatalities can be charged to these grandstanding exhibits.

In contemplating these early casualty lists, one notices that the Wright machine, in fact most biplane types, were high on the list. The accident at Fort Myer in which Lieutenant Selfridge was killed can be charged to the biplane design. This accident was initiated by a faulty propeller, but the machine fell from a height of only 50 to 80 feet while out of control. Had Selfridge been accommodated within a fuselage cockpit, instead of sitting out on the edge of the lower wing, he might have come out of the incident unscathed. But there was no seat, as such; no seat belt, and nothing but a frail interplane strut to cling to. The pilot, Orville Wright, had at least two sturdy hand levers to take much of the shock, and he had only a broken thigh. Selfridge, however, was tossed forward and apparently received a severe skull fracture.

After Selfridge's death, there were no more fatal accidents for almost a year, but on September 7, 1909, Eugene Lefebvre, a very clever airman who even then was known as a "trick flier," was killed while testing a new Wright biplane at the Juvisy aerodrome in France. This machine was one of the first produced by the French company licensed to build and sell the Wright biplane. In this case it was obvious that some portion of the control system had jammed, or that, after a good take-off and some level flight, the plane suddenly nosed toward the ground with engine full on and crashed. Lefebvre was thrown out and killed.

Two weeks later Captain Ferdinand Ferber, mentioned earlier, was killed while flying a Voisin in a demonstration at Boulogne. This machine, not greatly unlike the one flown by Henri Farman, was actually on the ground and running along on its wheeled gear, but it dropped into a ditch. The aeroplane was wrecked, and the engine that was mounted behind the pilot was torn from its bearers, falling forward on the pilot. Ferber suffered injuries from which he never recovered. This accident indicated another grave defect in the pusher-biplane design, and many critics immediately pointed out the peril the airman faced aboard any machine with its engine mounted behind him. It was argued that in the tractor-monoplane design the pilot not only sat in comparative comfort and security within the fuselage, but he had the engine up front where in many instances it would take much of the initial shock should an accident occur. The supporters of the Wright models stated that in the biplane with the engine, or engines, behind the pilot, the airman did not suffer the discomfort of propeller wash whipping past his face. As pointed out before, the Wright concern did not attempt to build a biplane with a sheltered cockpit until 1915, and in this model they still retained the dual, pusher propellers driven from an engine mounted inside the fuselage—but still behind the pilot.

Near the end of 1909 a great crowd witnessed another fatal accident when Señor Fernandez was killed at Nice, France, while flying a lightweight biplane patterned on Glenn Curtiss's *June Bug*. This machine that structurally had been pared to the utmost to meet the limitations of its power plant, had been flown successfully several times. During one of these flights Señor Fernandez crossed the airfield at a height of several hundred feet when his biplane suddenly collapsed in midair and whirled to the ground. His wife who was watching the flight saw him killed on the spot. In this case all aeronautical experts, such as they were, agreed that the structural weakness of the machine was the cause of the fatality, and it was pointed out that all factors of safety were more important than any attempts to lighten standard structure to obtain extra speed.

The Loss of Delagrange

The fifth mechanical-flight airman to die was the popular Léon Delagrange, who was equally well known as a sculptor, and winner of the Prix de Rome. He had become interested in flying when he had watched the first experiments of the Voisin brothers at Issy-les-Moulineaux. He eventually took up the sport, and made a number of short flights with the Voisin box-kite biplanes. At one time he was Henri Farman's competitor for the "duration" record which at that time was computed in minutes rather than hours.

After several months of the Voisin influence, Delagrange designed a biplane of his own, and then went to Louis Blériot's school where he learned to fly a Blériot monoplane.

The French sculptor flew in one of these machines at the Doncaster, England, aviation meeting held in 1909. Toward the end of this competition there arrived for him a new and very interesting monoplane from France. It was a Blériot, the first to be fitted with a Gnome rotary engine, a 7 cylinder plant that produced 50 horsepower. The Blériots had previously been powered with a 3-cylindered Anzani that developed 25 horsepower. The Gnome raised the speed of the Blériot to 40 miles per hour, and Delagrange gained many of the honors that were flown for at Doncaster.

After the British meet, Delagrange had this Gnome-powered Blériot sent to Pau, France, where Blériot had a large flying school. In January 1910, Delagrange began a series of tests to determine the advantages of this new machine. On January 4, despite a gusty wind that hampered his tests, Delagrange was flying past the hangars of the field when an unusually strong blast caught his monoplane. Those who witnessed the accident said that one of the wings collapsed under the strain, and although the machine did not fall from a very great height, it struck the ground with such force the monoplane was totally wrecked and Delagrange killed.

On April 2, 1910, Hubert Le Blon, another Frenchman who had competed with Delagrange at Doncaster, was killed in a tragic accident. Le Blon had been a well-known automobile racer who had learned to fly under Louis Blériot, and favored the Blériot monoplane. At Doncaster Le Blon used an Anzani-powered machine and showed great daring against strong winds, but after that meeting he decided to try a Blériot powered with the Gnome, and with a machine of this type he entered an aviation meet at San Sebastián, Spain.

After a formal luncheon given by the municipal authorities of the town, Le Blon agreed to make a flight out over

the sea, possibly to raise interest in the coming program.
After a successful take-off, the airman flew beyond the
crowded beaches, and then started to return. There were
several versions of what actually happened, but most eye-
witnesses explained that they saw the monoplane approach
the shore, and then suddenly nose into the water. There
were some rocks just below the surface on which the
machine lay just submerged. When a boat reached the spot
Le Blon was found still in his seat, but unconscious, and
he died soon after being removed from the wreck. It was
clear, it was said, that he had been knocked senseless by
the shock and had drowned. No one could agree what
caused the accident, although some reports stated that his
engine had failed. Another theory was that Le Blon had
been taken ill while flying, and had lost control of his
machine.

An unusual accident on May 13, 1910, took the life of
Hauvette-Michelin, a young, and most enthusiastic begin-
ner. This popular French sportsman had been learning to
fly an *Antoinette* monoplane at Chalons, and, though not
entirely proficient, had been persuaded to appear with his
machine at an aviation meeting at Lyons. On this day in
question he brought his *Antoinette* out for an early morning practice flight. After a successful take-off and a short
circuit he landed, but before coming to a halt on the ground
he collided with one of the wooden pylons that had been
erected to mark the circular course. Hauvette-Michelin had
landed safely, but on striking the pylon the upper half of it
broke away and fell on the little aeroplane, killing the pilot.

More aviation fatalities darkened the headlines of the
newspapers of 1910. On June 18 of that year T. Robl, the
first German to die in a heavier-than-air craft, was killed
while flying in a strong wind at Stettin, Germany. On

July 3 another French sportsman, Charles Wachter, who was considered to be one of the most skilled *Antoinette* pilots, was killed while making an altitude flight. He was diving down from the 1000-foot level at a rather steep angle when both wings suddenly folded back like a folio, and with the engine still running, the machine struck the center of the aerodrome, killing Wachter instantly.

British aviation suffered a severe loss in the death of Charles S. Rolls on July 12, 1910. It will be remembered that he had made a down payment on the first Wright biplane to be built in France. From the time of its delivery, and his training in flying the machine, Rolls had become one of Britain's outstanding airmen.

Shortly after the Reims competition another international meet was held at Bournemouth, England. Along with several other British airmen, Rolls had agreed to compete, and for the schedule of events he was flying the ordinary type of Wright biplane with one important modification. In the first place, the French models were being equipped with wheeled undercarriages, and to facilitate the take-off a new type of tail plane had been devised and set behind the twin rudders. This horizontal plane was operated in conjunction with the front elevating planes. In other words, in addition to helping the biplane to rise, this new rear-elevating plane also tended to increase the stability of the machine when in flight. From all accounts this rear plane was patterned after those that had been fitted to the Farman and other type biplanes of the era.

It should be explained that this control system was new to Rolls, as it had been fitted to the machine he was flying just the day before. Before noon on the day of the fatality Rolls decided to make an attempt to win what today would be called a spot-landing prize. The plan was to take off, fly a circuit of the field, and land as close as possible to a circle whitewashed on the aerodrome just in front of the grandstand.

Rolls took off from a point near the hangars, rose to about 150 feet, moved away with the wind and circled behind the grandstand. It was obvious that he intended to make another turn and approach the marker, flying against the wind. The day was perfect for flying with a fairly strong but steady breeze. He continued to climb until he had about 200 feet and then made his turn to approach the landing field. By the time he was down to 150 feet he appeared to be gliding in at a very steep angle with his engine still full on. He continued in this manner until he was down to 100 feet and less than 60 yards from the whitewashed circle. Onlookers saw Rolls attempting to pull the biplane out of this steep dive, and then the plane suddenly seemed to stand still in the air. There was an ominous crack, and it was seen that the new horizontal elevating plane was coming loose from its supports. It fluttered for an instant, twisted on its hinge and swung around to a vertical position.

Next, there was a grinding noise from the rear of the machine, and the biplane started to break up. In seconds parts of the structure were fouling the whirling propellers. All equilibrium had been lost by now. The nose went down at a steep angle, and the machine plunged to the field from a height of 80 feet. Charles Rolls was instantly killed.

Whether this accident was caused by structural failure, or a sudden gust of wind that brought on frantic overcontrolling thus resulting in the structural failure, has never been confirmed.

The following day saw another aeroplane fatality when Daniel Kinet was killed while flying a Farman biplane from

Ghent to Selzeate, Belgium. Kinet was a highly skilled cross-country flier, but after starting off safely and making good progress he was forced to descend because of engine trouble. He landed without incident, but collided with a tree at the end of his landing run, a collision that was sufficient to overturn the aeroplane, and Kinet who was trapped beneath the wreckage was killed.

A month later Nicholas Kinet, presumably a brother of Daniel, was killed while flying a Farman. In this instance Nicholas was caught in a very high wind at altitude, and fell completely out of control.

The Fate of Georges Chavez

As is evident, the year 1910 was marked by many aviation fatalities as dozens of sportsmen became interested in flying. There were many opportunities to show their skill and daring, but all too often these qualities outranged the power and structural specifications of their mounts. After the Kinets were killed, five more daring aeronauts paid the penalty during August and September, including the famous Georges Chavez who was killed while landing at Domodossola, Italy, after making a remarkable flight over the Alps.

Georges Chavez was a Peruvian running champion who became a skillful Blériot pilot, and his fatal exploit first thrilled, then shocked the aviation fraternity. Just twenty-three years old, Chavez had swept through the aviation world like a human comet and was the toast of the Parisian boulevards. At the Blackpool (England) meet in August he set a new altitude record of 5864 feet, and later pushed this mark up to 8127 feet.

A short while later the Aero Club of Milan, Italy, held an aviation meet, and to highlight the program of attractions offered a prize of about $15,000 for the first flight from Brig, Switzerland, over the Alps and the Simplon Pass, and continuing on to land at the Milan field. Every feature of this flight presented great hazards. The take-off field was too small and was at least 2000 feet above sea level where the air was comparatively thin. The summit of the Simplon Pass rose to 6582 feet, and the route dared a long, tortuous wind-tunnel valley that lay between the Fletschhorn (13,127 feet) and Monte Leone (11,684 feet), and then down to Domodossola and the warm sunshine of an Italian valley. This was a daring, dangerous flight, from any point of view. Only five aviators filed entries.

The grim details of this gallant effort are remembered only faintly, but the tiny town of Brig was the focal point of the whole aviation world for three weeks. More than half a million words were sent out from its little telegraph office that usually handled four or five messages a day.

The weather was foul from the start and Chavez waited impatiently until September 23 when he was rewarded with some promise of a take-off. For days he had had a group of friends stationed on the top of Simplon to signal weather conditions by lighting a great bonfire which the Peruvian watched hour after hour through a telescope. The minute he saw the smoke column rise straight up, he made his final preparations to get away. Clouds, heavy with moisture, hung between the great peaks, and a cold drizzle was falling in Brig. Although snow was whitening the flanks of Monte Leone there were no treacherous winds. None of the other entrants wanted to risk a take-off, and tried to dissuade Chavez from making the attempt at that time, but he would not be stayed.

He dressed warmly for the flight by first drawing on a complete suit of impermeable Chinese paper, over which he wore a waterproof coverall that was quilted with cotton, a thick sweater, and a leather shooting jacket. In addition he had a crash helmet, rubber goggles, and mountaineering boots. While he prepared his plane, a cavalcade of cars bearing doctors, mechanics, and Alpine guides set off by road. More signal fires were lit along Napoleon's road, guiding the way to Domodossola, while the rest of the course to Milan was marked with buoys on Lake Maggiore. To top it all a powerful acetylene beacon was set up and lighted on the highest point of the Simplon.

Chavez took off from the pocket-handkerchief field, and for more than fifteen minutes his Blériot monoplane seemed to disappear into the pine-covered slopes of the hills. But he climbed steadily and followed the winding road up the Simplon until at last the anxious watchers in Brig picked him out. It is said that the Augustinian monks of the famed hospice prayed for him as he swept over the summit of the pass, flying at 8000 feet, and then raced on over the Gondo Gorge, as the thud and roar of his Gnome engine started an avalanche and sent rocks cascading down the sheer walls. Success had flown with him so far, and he planned to land at Domodossola to refuel before continuing on to Milan. After forty minutes of flying time he had crossed the Alps, following the route that had taken the legions of Hannibal and Napoleon two weeks to conquer.

At Domodossola hundreds of anxious people saw him fly triumphantly down the wide, friendly valley from the mountains and make a perfect approach to the prepared landing ground. Success seemed to be within reach when for no apparent reason, the Blériot monoplane failed to level off, and nosed sharply into the ground from a height of about 15 feet. The Blériot hit hard and made a complete somersault. Chavez was pinioned in the wreckage with both legs broken. But his injuries proved to be more serious than at first thought, and he died four days later in a hospital just half an hour before a delegation from the Milan Aero Club had arrived to tell him that he had been awarded a consolation prize of $10,000. The Alps were not conquered again for three years.

Later consideration of Chavez's crash leaned toward the possibility that the pilot had become so numbed with the cold during the flight over the Alps that he could not make the necessary movement of his control levers when nearing the ground.

Ralph Johnstone Joins the List

It was an American, Lieutenant Selfridge, who was the first to die in an aircraft crash (September 17, 1908), but it was fourteen months later before another American was killed. He was Ralph Johnstone, a former vaudeville performer, who was something of a trick flier with the Wright brothers team.

Over a period of public exhibitions Johnstone had devised what was billed as a "spiral glide" with which he usually climaxed his performance. He would nose down in a steep dive with his engine on, and then pull up a few feet from the ground, bank hard, and climb away in a sharp spiral. On November 20, 1910, Johnstone was giving an exhibition at Denver, and again he ended his program with the widely advertised spiral glide, but on this occasion something went wrong; once he had pulled up from the sharp dive and gone into the tight bank, some portion of his machine collapsed, and Johnstone was instantly killed.

Two more American airmen were killed in quick succession. The first was John B. Moisant who was killed at New Orleans while flying a Blériot on December 31, 1910, and the same day Archie Hoxsey was killed at Los Angeles while flying a Wright biplane.

John Moisant was a typical American adventurer, and it is surprising he has not been written about by more authors of thriller stories, or by the Hollywood scenario writers. A native of Chicago, Illinois, he took an active part in five Central American revolutions before he was thirty-five. Learning of the many aeroplane flights that were holding the attention of Europe, President José Santos Zelaya of Nicaragua sent Moisant to Paris to purchase a Blériot monoplane.

Once in Europe, with the machine bought and six flying lessons in his book, Moisant decided to make better use of President Zelaya's machine, and announced that he would fly from Paris to London, a feat that as yet had not been attempted—but not only that, he would also carry a passenger. This flight was one of aviation's epics.

Learning of Moisant's intent, Hubert Latham, a first-class British airman, decided to make it a friendly race, so they both took off together from Issy-les-Moulineaux. Moisant flew the Blériot with a mechanic, Albert Filieux, as his passenger, and Latham was aboard an *Antoinette*. Latham beat Moisant over the first leg from Paris to Amiens, but damaged his undercarriage in landing there, and decided to withdraw.

Spending the night in Amiens, Moisant and Filieux rested and planned their next hop. After breakfast they continued on and reached Calais where they landed to refuel. Then, although the weather was rough and the Channel shrouded in patches of mist, the American risked everything and made the crossing. Albert Filieux was the first to fly the Channel as a passenger in an aeroplane, and Moisant's was the fifth crossing of the 23-mile strip of water.

They landed in a field of oats some six miles inland from Dover where Harry Harper, Lord Northcliffe's intrepid aviation correspondent, found them. He was amazed to learn that Moisant had made the trip relying entirely on a pocket compass, allowing for wind and flying by guess and by God.

Moisant needed 20 litres of castor oil for the Gnome engine, and after a night of sleeping in a haystack, he and his passenger continued on, heading for Canterbury, but had to land at Sittingbourne, having fractured a valve stem. Filieux repaired it in a short time, and they made another start. This time they covered only ten miles when fouled plugs forced them down in a country garden near Rainham. The ground was soft, the wheels sank in, and both undercarriage and propeller were damaged. Checking the map they found that they were still 25 miles short of their goal.

Instead of giving up, Moisant telegraphed to Paris for a new propeller while a group of Royal Engineers from Chatham welded his broken undercarriage. The propeller arrived by express delivery, and within 24 hours they were again on their way to London. After flying about three miles, they came down again—in the excitement both Moisant and Filieux had forgotten to fill the gas tank. They landed near Gillingham.

This time inclement weather grounded them for two days, but on August 23, in the face of a terrific gale, Moisant took off again, but after an hour found that he had covered only 19 miles and had to land at Wrotham for more gasoline. They took off again, made four miles, and then crash-landed on the estate of Sir Mark Collet near Sevenoaks where they accepted the hospitality of the Englishman until the undercarriage was repaired with the help of the village blacksmith. Before they took off again, Lady Collet, who was an invalid, asked them to fly within sight of her bedroom window. Moisant graciously agreed, and in so doing almost came to grief in an apple tree, but he managed to clear, and stagger on to London.

After as wild a career as any pioneer aviator, John Moisant finally met his end at New Orleans while flying during a very gusty wind. He had argued for months that if aeroplanes were to have any practical use, they would have to be built to fly in all weather, but he died while trying to make his point.

One of the most popular airmen of his time, Archie Hoxsey lost his life on the day that saw the end of Moisant, while piloting a Wright biplane in an exhibition flight at Los Angeles. As he was gliding from a considerable height, his machine appeared to snap out of control, turn over in the air, and tumble to earth. Hoxsey was killed, and at first it was announced that some part of the machine had collapsed, but this was changed later to Hoxsey's losing consciousness "owing to his very rapid descent," and being unable to control the machine. Hubert Latham, who saw the accident, attributed it to an "air hole," and in that statement probably established the old "air pocket" explanation for every aviation accident. There are, of course, no "air pockets" in the atmosphere. It has long been established that nature abhors a vacuum.

The year 1910 saw the end of another of England's beloved airmen, Cecil Grace. He was competing in the Baron de Forest $20,000 prize for the longest flight from Great Britain to the Continent by a Briton in an all-British ma-

chine before December 31, 1910. A number of British pilots
had entered the event, but all of them waited until December before making their bids. However, on December 18,
T. O. M. Sopwith who became one of Britain's greatest
aircraft designers and producers of war planes, took off
from Eastchurch aboard a Howard T. Wright biplane and
reached Hainaut, Belgium—a distance of 177 miles.

Determined to beat that mark, Cecil Grace set off from
the same Eastchurch field with a Short-built Wright biplane. He actually crossed the Channel, but came down at
Les Baraques near Calais because he had encountered an
adverse wind that he thought would prevent his beating
Sopwith's effort. So he decided to turn back and head for
Dover to try again.

After a lunch at Calais, Grace took off and headed back
to England with a number of steam tugs marking his course.
The afternoon was bright and sunny at Calais, but weather
reports indicated that Grace might find some fog once he
neared the English shore. A southwest wind was blowing
at about 10 miles per hour near the ground, but might reach
20 miles per hour at higher levels.

Grace was seen to take off and head for England, but an
experienced seaman aboard one of the tugs observed that
the Englishman did not seem to be holding the correct
course for Dover. Other seamen spotted him at times, and
once he was reported near the East Goodwin lightship
which indicated he was well off course, and apparently flying in a northerly direction. He was never seen again, and
probably came down somewhere in the North Sea. It is said
that he was the first aviator to lose his life in the sea.

The aeroplane was suffering growing pains, as had all
other means of locomotion, but in flight there were many
more critical factors to consider. Structural failure was up-

permost, and strangely enough, engine failure could be blamed in very few instances. Attracted by the rich prizes, men were hurriedly building hopeless contraptions, using unsuitable materials and workmanship that would not have been tolerated in a third-rate bicycle shop. First-class wing spars were being attached to the fuselage with tiny bolts and brackets that could not take sudden strain. Some men tried aluminum castings long before that metal had been tested fully. Others employed unbelievable combinations of brass, copper, or strip iron. In their anxiety to compete for the headlines and monetary prizes many self-trained pilots took hopeless risks, and all too often paid the Great Penalty.

CHAPTER VII

The Great Colonel Cody

The Flying Cathedral • The Channel Flight • Latham's Gallant Failure • Enter Louis Blériot • The Reims Competitions • Aviation Meets Galore • Good Old Blackpool! • The Great Manchester Race • An Epic Contest • Flight by Moonlight

---

A new breed of newspaperman was developed with the advance of the aeroplane; a fabulous figure who became known as an air correspondent. He was usually a young man of limited literary ability, but long on adventure. Often he was a devotee of high-speed motorcars and motorcycles, and never above risking his neck in a balloon ascension or aboard an experimental glider. Today's aviation reporters are a colorless tribe compared to the air correspondents of 1905–10.

One of the first of these was the famous Harry Harper who was born to journalism in 1880, being the son of a man who edited a group of periodicals dealing with the food and wine trade. Young Harry's world hummed with high-wheel bicycles and had reached the period when cycle races were a great sport and pastime. In the early 1890s the first motorcars began to appear on European and British roads, and a few balloons were floating about the country-side usually advertising soaps, perfumes, or patent medicines. Harper was early entranced with books that dealt with man's first attempts to fly, and later on he read the works of H. G. Wells, and Jules Verne.

He enjoyed his first flutter in the aviation field when he was working for a provincial paper and was assigned to cover a summer fete that featured a famous trio of balloonists, the Spencer brothers, Arthur, Stanley, and Percival. Their act included a "Professor Fleet" who made a descent by parachute. In London Harper worked for the *Music Hall and Theatre Review* and while there encountered an American, Samuel Franklin Cody, who was producing a Wild West extravaganza titled *The Klondike Nugget*. This man, who billed himself as Colonel Cody but was not related to Buffalo Bill, unwittingly led Harry Harper into the field of aviation reporting, where he became the greatest air correspondent in the early part of the twentieth century.

This introduction to Harry Harper in turn brings onto the scene the man who was to build and fly the first successful aeroplane in Great Britain. An American from his sombrero to the heels of his cowboy boots, he is completely unknown in the land of his birth, but when all factors are considered he was as important in his time as either of the Wrights, Glenn Curtiss, or Dr. Christmas. Had he lived, let us say, through World War I, he might have become one of the outstanding figures in the world of aviation.

An old, gnarled oak tree, protected by an ornamental iron railing, still stands on what was once known as Laffan's

Plain, now Farnborough the present cradle of British aviation. A commemorative tablet embedded in concrete states:

Colonel S. F. Cody picketed his aeroplane to this tree, and from near this spot on May 16, 1909 made the first successful, officially recorded flight in Great Britain.

This famous flight brought an end to a frantic period of frustration when many British experimenters tried to build something that would fly. They had failure after failure with their gas-filled airships; there had been one called hopefully the *Mayfly*, which didn't—or wouldn't—and another with the classic title *Nulli Secundus* (second to none) that ended on the discard heap, practically a nonstarter in the international gasbag sweepstakes.

Cody, who became a naturalized British subject, was successful in what was practically his first attempt. A year before he had bounced through a few, small, insignificant hops, using an old *Antoinette* engine taken from a speedboat, and when some official prize money was put up, the Yankee colonel lost little time in proving that he indeed could aviate.

Data and statistics concerning Samuel Franklin Cody are vague and bewildering. It is said that he was born on the outskirts of Fort Worth, Texas, about 1861. His parents were immigrants from Ulster who were most peripatetic, seldom staying long anywhere. Samuel's schooling is somewhat a mystery, but he was a born inventor and a skilled mechanic. In his early years he went to the Klondike in search of gold, but was not successful, and he had to draw on the robes of a strolling player in the honky-tonk circuit of that day. Usually assuming the role of the villain, Cody disclaimed and chewed up the scenery night after night. He also painted the flats, tuned the piano, and created most of the lighting effects used throughout the deep-freeze itinerary. Away from the footlights he assumed the role of the professional cowboy, and twirled a lariat with the best of them. When the famous Buffalo Bill (William Frederick Cody) rose to international stardom, Samuel Franklin Cody was not above filching chunks of the other Cody's aura, brazenly using the title of colonel. Whenever he was in funds he rode a milk-white horse, buckled a silver-mounted belt about his middle, and gave astonishing performances as a pistol marksman. One of his prize acts was to drive tenpenny nails at a distance of 50 feet.

Whether he wished to extend his operations, or he was chased out of the Yukon, is not known, but Cody appeared in England in 1890. While he amused the British natives with his fringed costumes and cowboy hardware, he was not above appearing on the provincial stage as an actor, tackling anything from Shakespeare to the famous old melodrama of the Gay Nineties, *Mariah Martin,* or *The Murder in the Red Barn.*

In fairness, it should be said that Cody's cowboy display was a deceptive veneer. He was a man of sterling character and amazing ability and had a gentlemanly manner that endeared him to men and women alike. His courage and indomitable spirit were beyond question, and though his fame never matched that of the original Buffalo Bill, his exploits were more stirring from the point of scientific advance.

During the year 1901 Cody was starring in his own thriller *The Klondike Nugget* at a theater in Liverpool. George Fyfe, a London newspaperman who had gone up to interview him, had been warned to expect a picturesque figure, but he was surprised to find Cody flying a gigantic kite in one of the public parks.

"What's the idea?" Fyfe asked him, as the Merseyside urchins were having a glorious time with this unusual play-mate.

"Oh, this is something I have been interested in for a long time," Cody explained. "I have been working on the idea of coupling a number of kites like this, hanging a basket below, and lifting a man up to a considerable height."

"What for?" inquired Mr. Fyfe, probably scratching his head.

"Just think of its value during a war. This idea will enable one to view the countryside from above, and perhaps even take photographs of important areas."

The London newspaperman pondered on this, and began to see the value of man-carrying kites. This was months before anyone had really thought of using the heavier-than-air flying machine for reconnaissance purposes. When Fyfe got back to London he casually dropped a word about Colonel Cody's kite-flying to an imaginative member of the British Admiralty.

Cody continued his kite experiments during the next few years and actually made a few ascents himself. He gained his first aviation headline in 1904 when he flew a man up to 1600 feet by means of a number of kites flown in tandem. The Admiralty then decided to call in Colonel Cody for a long talk. Until that time the American had only one kite-flying rival in Great Britain, Major B. F. S. Baden-Powell, who was working on a similar idea for the Army and the War Office.

The Admiralty put Cody aboard a warship where his man-carrying kite technique was passed on to a new corps of Naval observers, and for some years the British Navy used these kites in their gun-spotting and reconnaissance work. The American was awarded $20,000 for these efforts, and gave up the greasepaint and footlights for a time.

In 1903 Cody had the idea of having a set of his man-carrying kites haul him across the Strait of Dover from England to France. With a *Daily Mail* reporter, William Maitland, Cody climbed into a light canvas boat that was hooked to a tandem-formation of his kites. A favorable wind did pull them out a couple of miles, but it was found that when the boat moved at a reasonable rate of speed, the kites sagged down. Cody tried towing a sea anchor, or drogue, but the favoring tide added to the boat's speed which was too much for the kites, and the novel project had to be given up.

That year, of course, the Wright brothers made their first successful series of flights at Kitty Hawk, and on hearing the news, Cody forgot about man-carrying kites, and concentrated on building an aeroplane.

While he was pondering on the Wrights' accomplishment, he was induced to work with the Royal Engineers who were responsible for what was considered to be military aviation at that time. The Engineers had taken over the military kite balloon, and several of Britain's less fortunate, lighter-than-air projects in order to compete with Count Zeppelin's dirigibles. Between 1904–07 Cody became a balloon pilot, and was closely associated with the British Army's balloon factory at Laffan's Plain, Aldershot.

With Colonel J. E. Capper and Colonel J. Templer of the Balloon Corps, Cody designed and helped to build Great Britain's first dirigible *Nulli Secundus* which was 111 feet in length and capable of carrying three people at a speed of 20 miles per hour. Instead of employing the usual balloon cloth of cotton or silk combined with rubber, the gasbag was made of eight layers of goldbeater's skin—about as expensive a material as could be found for the purpose, because it is made from the lining of the digestive tract of animals. About 60,000 carcasses were needed to furnish a sufficient amount to make the envelope.

Nulli Secundus proved to be an also-ran, and was dismantled and hidden away for months. The $20,000 prize money Cody had won for his man-carrying kites was soon exhausted and he had to return to the country fairs and provincial theaters to finance further experiments. He organized a rootin', tootin' cowboy troupe that performed on British racecourses through 1906–07, and he finally saved enough money to build a powered aeroplane.

The Flying Cathedral

When Cody built his aeroplane, he built big, just as he had with his kites. While his original design was based on his early box kites, he really spread out when he ventured into the powered aircraft field. Dubbed *The Flying Cathedral*, it had a wingspan of 52 feet, and towered to a height of 9 feet. Everything about it was generous in size. The front elevators and rudders carried as much fabric as a present-day light plane. It weighed just over 2000 pounds, and if we consider that today's Lockheed T-33 jet trainer has a wingspan of only 38 feet, 10 inches, and that Louis Blériot's cross-Channel monoplane weighed less than 500 pounds we can get some idea of the proportions of Colonel Cody's brain child.

Thirty horsepower was about as much as any man dared deal with in an aircraft in 1908, but Cody started with a 50-horsepower *Antoinette* engine that twirled two 8-foot propellers, driven by a complicated system of bicycle chains

—just as the Wrights had done. He used up enough bamboo to build a Chinese pagoda, but each bamboo member was wrapped tightly in steel wire or linen cord between the joints to prevent splitting. The pilot sat on a crude seat, a metal saddle affair pilfered from a riding plow, and the passenger—when one was carried—sat in another in tandem, but slightly higher.

In truth, Cody's biplane had many features of the Wright brothers' invention, but it was almost twice as large, and though they had employed wing-warping for lateral stability, Cody devised a system of wing-warping to which he co-ordinated the inverse movement of two halves of his elevation rudder (elevator).

Cody's control column consisted of a massive wooden stanchion on which was mounted a small bicycle wheel. The stanchion was moved back and forth to depress or raise the nose. The wheel was connected to the rudders. Later on, after some modification of his design, he dispensed with the wing-warping system, and mounted a couple of billboard-sized ailerons between the two outer bay struts.

Early in 1908 Cody made short test hops, getting the feel of the monster, and it has been reported reliably that he made enough progress to be credited with actually flying in that year. It is pointed out, however, that he was never more than 10 or 12 inches off the ground, and his detractors argued that he had just been lawn-mowing. He made several flights of about 75 yards at this height, but his efforts were no better than those of several British experimenters. On October 16, 1908, Cody remained in the air for 27 seconds, covering a distance of 1390 feet, but unfortunately this effort was not observed by the Royal Aero Club officials whose word was necessary to get Cody's name in the record books.

Ignoring the prestige that might have come with being credited as the first man to fly an aeroplane in Great Britain in that year, Cody returned his machine to the sheds, and worked on improving the design while he again trod the boards to raise money for further experiments. He abandoned the 50-horsepower *Antoinette* engine, and remembering the 80-horsepower E.N.V. that had been used aboard old *Nulli Secundus*, he induced officials of the Royal Engineers to turn it over to him. This power plant gave him what he needed to get his gigantic aircraft to greater heights, and the speed necessary to provide efficient control.

On February 22, 1909, Colonel Cody, still performing before no one more important than a few laborers digging a ditch, made a straightaway flight of over 400 yards. Surprised to find how well the *Cathedral* acted with its new engine, he attempted to fly *into* the wind that was blowing at 12 miles per hour. He had been laboring under the delusion that to fly *with* the wind would greatly help his engine and propellers, so he was astonished to feel the craft climbing skyward with no trouble at all. He was so pleased with this performance, he decided to risk his neck and make a turn—something he had not attempted heretofore. As the ditchdiggers on the ground looked up in amazement, the *Flying Cathedral* climbed several hundred feet, slithered through a 180-degree turn, and went back to land a few feet from where it had taken off.

It is not known how many such amateur attempts Cody made before he put in his bid for official recognition, but on May 16 of that year he invited members of the Royal Aero Club to come out to Laffan's Plain to witness what antics he could perform. This time he was the showman once more, appearing in a white motoring duster and white golf cap, with his waxed mustaches protruding like Cossacks' lances. Then, to the wonder of the Aero Club officials, he tied the tail of his machine to a butcher's large springbalance that was fastened to the gnarled oak tree. He climbed into the pilot's seat, opened the E.N.V. engine, and let the two propellers whirl. He climbed down again and went back to look at the spring-balance to assure himself that the engine was "pulling its revs" by noticing how far up the scale the indicator had been drawn. Once his power plant and propellers were performing efficiently, Cody untied the machine and took off for a flight of more than four miles!

The British officials were so impressed they immediately ordered that a commemorative plaque be erected—probably to mark their own amazement as well as Cody's flying achievement. In September of that year Colonel Cody, by now a British subject, brought the world's cross-country record to England by flying a circular course in exactly 66 minutes.

From that time on this astounding showman was Britain's hero. He was headlined in all the important aero meets, and few spectators would turn up at the ticket window until they were assured that "Colonel" Cody—sombrero, silver spurs, and a full complement of Colt's hardware—would be on the bill. At one of these meets Cody entertained King George V with one of his unusual flying displays, and after the exhibition the King addressed Cody as "Colonel," a title that was accepted the world over from that day on.

By 1912 Cody was at the peak of his career. Long-distance flights were run-of-the-mill to him. He won every Michelin prize except one. In that year, too, when the British government put up $25,000 for the winning machine in the annual Military Trials, Cody built a two-place military biplane, and walked off with the money. This effort was the more remarkable as he was practically penniless at the time and competing against many European firms that had unlimited financial resources. This picturesque man did all his own repair work, servicing, and testing, and more often than not bought his gasoline and oil on the cuff.

But the Military Trials prize put him on his feet, and he soon was adding to his bank account with remunerative passenger flights. The Grim Reaper, however, caught up with him eventually—as it did so many other fliers—on August 7, 1913, when he was carrying a passenger named Evans. Cody's latest machine broke up in the air and both men were killed.

If Cody's early records are correct, he was fifty-two years old at the time of his death. He made his first aeroplane flight at age forty-seven, and had been floating about the sky inside the basket of a man-carrying kite when he was well over forty. Few men of this century have packed so much into so many years with such colorful display. Both the United States and Great Britain may be proud of this amazing character.

The Channel Flight

Harry Harper had first heard of Colonel Cody in 1903 and became interested in his man-carrying kites. He eventually wormed his way into the staff of Lord Northcliffe's *Daily Mail* and was appointed air correspondent, probably the first such post assigned to any newspaper reporter. His reception by the editor was decidedly lukewarm, for Harper was considered to be another liability foisted on him by the latest whim of the "Chief," but Harper was a

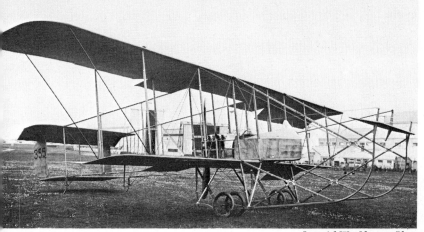

. Designed in 1910, this Farman S-7 Longhorn biplane was one of the first rcraft assigned to Royal Flying Corps squadrons. It was powered by a 75-hp enault engine, carried no armament, and had a top speed of 59 mph. In 10 the Longhorn held the world's distance record of 350 miles flown over closed circuit.

. The Farman Shorthorn was an improved version of the Longhorn, in ich the protruding forward elevator was eliminated. Many French squad- ns used these machines up until 1917. One flown by Escadrille M. F. 28 was first French aeroplane to be shot down by the Germans in World War I.

19. In 1912 the Deperdussin firm produced this military monoplane w
was accepted by Britain's Naval Air Service. It was powered with a 7
Gnome rotary engine and several saw service with coastal defense squad

20. The 1910 Bristol Boxkite, first British machine to go into factory
duction. In September of that year a Boxkite was flown during Army r
euvers, and air-to-ground radio transmission was successfully carried
Dozens of British airmen were trained on this machine and it became
basic aircraft on which the Bristol Aeroplane Company was founded.

21. The Wright "Baby" biplane of 1910. Built for racing competition and exhibitions. It was aboard this *Vin-Fiz* machine that Calbraith P. Rodgers of New York completed the first transcontinental flight from New York to Long Beach, California in 3 days, 10 hours, 4 minutes of flying time. Actually, 49 days were required to cover the 4231 miles.

22. Bristol Coanda monoplane, designed by Henri Coanda, a Rumanian. It crashed while competing in the 1912 Military Trials, killing two British Army airmen. With this, the War Office banned the monoplane for military purposes, but several were built and exported to Italy, Rumania, Bulgaria, and Germany.

Imperial War Museum Photo

23. The famous "Bloater" the B.E. 8a biplane which was among the first the Royal Aircraft factory's productions to go to war. Powered with an 80-Gnome it had a maximum speed of 70 mph. It had no ailerons but used wing warping for lateral control.

Imperial War Museum Photo

24. An early French Caudron G.II powered by a 45-hp Anzani engine. Many service pilots trained on this type and later in the war a clipped-wing version was designed on which student-pilots could make their first tentative hops

lucky man and his time brackets were perfect. He joined the *Daily Mail* in 1906 just as the aviation egg was beginning to crack, and men were sprouting wings in the incubation of progress. Harper spent the next two years covering the activities of balloon specialists, wondering about Count Zeppelin and his mighty dirigibles, and reading vague accounts of two brothers, named Wright, who were said to be flying regularly near a town called Dayton in far-off America. He heard about a Brazilian who was reported to have flown around the Eiffel Tower in Paris, and went over to interview this amazing man who told him of his determination to fly a heavier-than-air machine. Harper was not on hand when Santos-Dumont first flew his *canard* aircraft, but he was the first British reporter to write the story which had been telephoned to him from Paris by a colleague on the staff of the Continental *Daily Mail*.

"You're doing great work, my boy," Lord Northcliffe said, and congratulated him.

But Harry Harper's greatest thrill, and still most vivid of his many memories, was seeing Wilbur Wright fly at Le Mans in 1908. He became a favorite of both brothers and often dined with them at a nearby bistro. The young Englishman was to write many laudatory articles about the Wrights before they left Europe for the last time in 1909 and turned their attention to their American interests.

Harry Harper's news reports from Le Mans in which he vividly described Wilbur Wright's feats of flying, undoubtedly influenced Lord Northcliffe to offer the *Daily Mail* prize of $2500 for the first aeroplane flight across the Channel. This was first announced in 1908, but attracted little interest until the following year when Lord Northcliffe raised the prize money to $5000 (£1000). With this added inducement several pilots of skill and promise began to study the topography around Calais and Dover, and a number of French newspapers kept a force of reporters and photographers available for what they believed would be the greatest news story of the year.

Harry Harper checked in at the Terminus Hotel in Calais and planned to use the Marconi wireless system to get his story to London. The French government had given permission for a wireless station to be erected near Calais that would transmit to a second station set up on the roof of the Lord Warden Hotel in Dover from where Harper's story would be relayed by telephone to London.

Latham's Gallant Failure

The first pilot to appear with a real intent to risk the cross-Channel flight was the Anglo-Frenchman, Hubert Latham, a highly skilled *Antoinette* monoplane pilot. Latham had flown the Channel by balloon in 1904 from the Crystal Palace in London to a suburb of Paris. Later, he engaged in auto racing and big-game hunting. While racing motorboats at Monte Carlo, Latham met A. Levavasseur, the designer of the graceful *Antoinette* monoplane. Latham took his first flight on April 4, 1909, and soloed after a flight of only twenty minutes. The next day he flew for more than an hour, most of the time in a drenching downpour, lighting and smoking cigarettes to pass the time. Three months later Latham and Levavasseur were at Calais preparing to fly the Channel.

Latham's formal entry, giving the *Daily Mail* forty-eight hours' notice of an attempt to fly the Channel, caught the imagination of the public, and holiday crowds packed the beaches on both sides of the Strait of Dover. Every Chan-

nel steamer brought large numbers of journalists and excursionists to Calais, all hoping to see Latham and his
dainty *Antoinette*. Levavasseur and Latham chose a field
five miles from Calais at Sangatte and put up at the Hotel
de la Plage where the owner was soon in financial clover
with business booming until his wife gave birth to twins,
born prematurely because of all the excitement.

The enthusiasm was much the same in Dover; never had
so many people watched the Channel since the days of Napoleon's threatened invasion. Everything was on hand but
a spot of good weather. The crowds and Latham sat out
spells of high winds, rain, clouds, and fog from July 8 until July 19. Latham did risk a test flight on July 13, but
damaged his undercarriage while landing on the rough
field. Levavasseur and his mechanics soon repaired it, by
which time the wind had risen once more and the flight was
again postponed.

The next day all France hoped and prayed that Latham
would celebrate the glorious July 14, but rain made flying
impossible, so Levavasseur gave a party in the lounge of
the hotel. In Calais, Hart O. Berg arrived with the Count
de Lambert, Wilbur Wright's pupil, with plans to join in
the cross-Channel flight. This may have added to the excitement, but it lasted only a short time. The crowds began
to diminish on both sides of the Channel, and in France
the pressmen and photographers turned their attention to
the Wright camp at Wissant, a few miles from Sangatte
where the Count de Lambert was assembling two Wright
biplanes. In Dover interest in the promised Channel flights
lessened, and by July 17 British excursionists were flocking
to the Thames Estuary where the Home Fleet was staging
its annual review. The only other lively item in the news
concerning the heavier-than-air flight intimated that Hu-

bert Latham might be planning an espionage flight over the British fleet. It seemed that he was related to the newly elected Chancellor of Germany, Theobald von Bethmann-Hollweg, through his maternal grandmother, Mme. Arthur Mallet, a sister of the Chancellor. It was said that he was postponing his flight to coincide with the Home Fleet's display.

On July 19 Harry Harper arose from his hotel bed at 4:30, looked out the window and saw that although a thin drizzle still fell, a strong wind was blowing flocks of ragged clouds across the sky, but when he made contact with Dover he learned that the weather there was not favorable; fog, followed by wind and wet seemed the order of the day.

Half an hour later the weather promised to change, and when Levavasseur walked out of his hotel and looked up at the sky, there were some prospects of a sunny day. The Channel presented a smooth, pearly surface, and only a thin haze hid the white cliffs of Dover. By 5:30 visibility had reached ten miles, and Latham made up his mind to take his chance. At 6:42 he took off like a great dragonfly, and just as he became airborne, the sun broke through to put a golden sheen on the varnished fabric of the *Antoinette*. The French destroyer *Harpon* had taken up station a few miles off the cliffs below Sangatte. Levavasseur was on the bridge with the captain, determined to see his charge safely across the Channel.

Everything went well with the *Antoinette* and Latham flew directly over the destroyer. He was tempted to take a photograph of her as he looked down on the two funnels pouring out black smoke. But ill luck that had dogged the attempt for so long, cast its final spell. The 55-horse-power, 8-cylindered engine began to misfire. Latham immediately lost all interest in the destroyer below and searched for any form of electrical failure, but no immediate action had any effect. The engine quit cold, so there was nothing to do but attempt a landing on the water. Latham put the machine into a simple landing glide. The graceful monoplane settled on the water, and "floated like a cork." He swung his feet up onto a crossbar to keep them from getting wet, took out his case, lit a cigarette and waited for the *Harpon* to pick him up.

Latham and Levavasseur returned to Calais, and telegraphed an urgent message to the *Antoinette* factory in Paris for another machine.

Enter Louis Blériot

The day after Latham's unsuccessful attempt, Louis Blériot filed a formal entry with the editor of the Continental *Daily Mail,* and international excitement was whipped up again.

Blériot was totally unlike Latham. He was a stolid, deliberate man who had a deep-rooted enthusiasm for flying. He had spent much time and money on aeronautical research, and over the previous years had built a number of small monoplanes, most of which were unstable, and carried very sensitive controls. As a result, he suffered many serio-comic accidents, but led a charmed life. More important, he had a wise, understanding wife who managed his business affairs, took care of him when he was injured, and kept him in high spirits when luck ran against him.

By 1909 Blériot was a skilled pilot and sound businessman. He was one of the first to risk cross-country flying, and on July 13 while Latham was waiting at Sangatte for good Channel weather, Blériot made a magnificent flight of 25 miles from Etampes to Orléans, winning a prize of $2500 that had been put up by the Aero Club of France. During this flight his left foot was badly scalded by gasoline from the engine, and he had to walk on crutches for weeks, but this did not deter the indomitable Frenchman. He crated his *Blériot* XI and had it shipped by express to Calais. By coincidence it was placed aboard the same train that was hauling Latham's new *Antoinette*.

When it was taken from its van at Calais, it looked bleak, weary, and forlorn. Its wings were strapped to the sides of the fuselage, the wheels of the undercarriage were caked with mud, and its fabric was oil-streaked and travel-stained. It was the antithesis of Latham's new sleek *Antoinette*. An old white horse was harnessed to the aircraft which was then dragged through the streets of Calais to the farm of M. Grigon in Les Baraques, not far from Sangatte. On hand to greet Blériot were Alfred Leblanc, his business associate; M. Anzani, designer of the 24-horsepower engine that powered the monoplane; and two mechanics, Collin and Mamet.

Now three airmen were preparing for a Channel flight. Latham and Levavasseur were working day and night at Sangatte. Blériot was soon ready at Les Baraques, and at Wissant the Count de Lambert had the first of his Wright biplanes ready for a test flight. The newspaper reporters were staging frantic races to keep up with the three camps, until early one morning while making a test flight the Count de Lambert had engine trouble and wrecked his machine on landing. That put him out of the race, as his second machine would not be assembled for some time.

Latham's *Antoinette* was ready by the morning of July 23, but again he had to wait for favorable conditions; a gale that lasted forty-eight hours kept everyone indoors.

Both Latham and Blériot observed every formality of good breeding. The former paid a call on his rival in the Terminus Hotel where they politely discussed the recent cross-country flight. Later in the day Blériot drove out to Sangatte and admired the beautiful finish and workmanship of the *Antoinette*.

The French Navy found itself in a service row. The *Harpon* had been replaced by a faster destroyer, the *Escopette*, which had orders to escort an aeroplane across the Channel, but the orders were not specific about which aeroplane was to be escorted. Blériot suggested that the *Escopette* naturally should escort the first machine to take off, but Latham claimed prior rights, pointing out that he had been the first contestant to turn up at Calais. The skipper of the destroyer added to the tempest by declaring that whatever the ruling, he would not put to sea on Sunday as his men deserved their regular holiday.

The gale continued all through that Saturday, and apparently Leblanc arose very early and decided that there was a chance of getting away by daylight. He aroused Blériot who took a gloomy view of the situation and admitted that he felt anything but fit. At Les Baraques, however, M. Anzani and the two mechanics were working on the battered monoplane under the glare of an acetylene lamp.

Still working on the story, Harry Harper learned by wireless that the weather in Dover was not too promising either; there was a light breeze, a few rain squalls, and the wind was expected to freshen during the day. He relayed this information to both camps. There was no activity at Latham's field at Sangatte. Latham's car was outside but the *Antoinette* was still under cover.

At 4:10 Blériot handed his crutches to his mechanics, climbed aboard and made a test flight, circling the area several times, and then came down to land. There still was no sign of activity at Latham's camp. The wind was gusty and the mechanics had to hang onto the monoplane as it stood on the ground, but Blériot and Leblanc decided that the attempt should be made before the weather worsened.

At 4:35 Blériot took off without benefit of compass or map. He simply asked a group of spectators, "In which direction is Dover?" A few hands pointed to the northwest, indicating where the chalk cliffs of Britain were hidden behind a pearly curtain. "Thank you," Blériot said, and opened the Anzani engine.

He wasted no time circling for altitude but flew straight as a dart for England. As he sped over the dunes not far from Sangatte, Levavasseur, who by then had crawled out to find out what the day was like, stood in amazement as he watched the *Blériot* XI vanish into the mist. He ran back and aroused Latham. Realizing that he had been outmaneuvered, Latham ordered his *Antoinette* brought out. He was determined to be the second man to fly the Channel.

Meanwhile Blériot was continuing his course. The captain of the *Escopette* who had changed his mind about sailing on Sunday was driving full speed ahead, and was at his station when Blériot overtook *Escopette* at a height of 240 feet. The wind freshened, and after ten minutes of flying, he had left the destroyer well behind. Then he found himself completely alone. He could not see the destroyer, nor could he see the coast of Britain, and for the next ten minutes he flew on without a compass.

He started to lose altitude rapidly, and it finally dawned on him that he had been flying at full throttle in order to stay in the air, and that the engine was overheating and losing power. (There is an apocryphal story that at this point Providence took a hand when he ran into a heavy rain squall. Water streamed down over the cylinders, ending the overheating.) This, of course, is most unlikely. The restoration of power must have been due to some other cause—a change in the electrical timing, for instance.

Blériot breathed a deep sigh of relief and continued on for another ten minutes when he at last spotted the green fields of England. After some cogitation he decided that he had been driven to the east and might be somewhere near St. Margaret's Bay, so he turned toward the west, and flew over the Home Fleet which lay at anchor below. He had to contend with strong headwinds but the little monoplane and its engine responded beautifully, and he finally nosed down toward the Shakespeare Cliff to select a wide green field for his historic touch down. He saw someone running across the North Fall meadow, waving a French flag to indicate where he might land, and with that assuring welcome, Blériot shut off his engine, and glided down, but a sudden down draft of air caught the little machine. Blériot pancaked very hard from about 60 feet, breaking his undercarriage and propeller. The time was 5:13 A.M. The first crossing of the English Channel by air had taken exactly 38 minutes.

When the news was received in Calais, Hubert Latham burst into tears, but quickly recovered and sent Blériot a telegram of warmest congratulations. Continued bad weather had halted any further attempts that day.

A tent was soon erected over the damaged monoplane, and visitors who paid sixpence for admission to look at the machine contributed £63 that was donated to the Dover hospitals and the police pension fund. That afternoon Louis

Blériot and his wife, who had come over on the *Escopette*, returned aboard the same vessel to Calais. As he walked down the gangplank Blériot was handed a telegram that stated he had been made a Chevalier of the Legion of Honor.

Lord Northcliffe's *Daily Mail* had a pointed editorial concerning the flight:

The event, which stirs the imagination by its far-reaching possibilities and marks the dawn of a new age for man, took place in the early hours of yesterday morning. Thus have the sceptics been put to scorn.

The British people have hitherto dwelt secure in their islands because they have attained at the price of terrible struggles and of immense sacrifices the supremacy of the sea. But locomotion is now being transferred to an element where Dreadnoughts are useless and sea power no shield against attack. As the potentialities of the aeroplane have been proved, we must take energetic steps to develop a navy of the air.

But ignoring all this, the British Parliament debated the laying down of four new superdreadnoughts to assure Great Britain's continued superiority over the Kaiser's navy.

The Berlin *Lokal Anzeiger* in Germany taunted: "England is no longer an island. Blériot flew as he liked."

In the United States the New York *American* said, "M. Blériot's feat will stir 10,000 inventors in America alone to try to improve on it."

The New York *Tribune* printed a caustic cartoon showing a bemused John Bull looking down on a fleet of dreadnoughts in the Channel and saying, "I was never made for flying." Five years later the Royal Flying Corps went on to glory and set up the victory of the First Battle of the Marne, and ended the war with the finest military air arm of that era.

The Reims Competitions

The excitement of Blériot's cross-Channel flight was just beginning to die down when the first organized flying meeting was opened at Reims. It was headlined as the *Grande Semaine d'Aviation de la Champagne* and was staged on the Plain of Bétheny, three miles outside the famous wine-making city of the Marne. Sixty thousand spectators turned up every day of the week-long show, some sitting in private boxes, others at the tables of the open-air restaurants, or crowded in the temporary stands. Many drank champagne under cool arbors, or joined the mobile throngs that gaped at the stilt-walkers, tight-rope artists, or the peep-shows. Aviation had become—in France at any rate—the world's greatest outdoor attraction.

The Reims meet introduced a new generation of pilots, among them A. Fournier, a well-known racing motorist; E. Bunau-Varilla, wealthy nephew of the owner of *Le Matin;* Roger Sommer, a manufacturer of cloth, and little Louis Paulhan, a mechanic who had won an engineless Voisin in a newspaper contest, and had taught himself to fly after his friends had chipped in to buy him a Gnome rotary engine. Among the other fliers was Eugene Lefebvre, an engineer and sportsman who was killed shortly after the Reims meet while test-flying a new Wright biplane.

One of the remarkable features of the meet was a record-breaking display by Henri Farman who flew a distance of 112 miles in 3 hours, 4 minutes over a measured course with his new Gnome-powered biplane, beating Hubert Latham's mark of 96½ miles the day before. One of the wildest ovations ever staged by an exhibition crowd greeted Farman's record. Railings were torn down, the police were scattered, and a screaming mass of enthusiastic people swept across the field to tow the biplane back to its hangar.

Before the full program had been completed more than half a million spectators had paid $175,000 to enter the grounds, and more than a million words were telegraphed by journalists assigned to cover the events. But the feature event was the $5000 prize put up by James Gordon Bennett for the highest speed over two laps, which was to be competed for annually.

The dark horse of the show was the American Glenn Hammond Curtiss, in fact the only American entered in the meet. All that was known of this man was that he had won a prize of some sort for making the first public flight of one mile in his native land. Other than that, Curtiss was just another American motorcyclist who had been associated with Professor Alexander Graham Bell's Aerial Experiment Association. He had arrived in France with a biplane called the *Golden Flyer* that was packed as personal baggage. At Reims he was interested only in winning the Gordon Bennett trophy, ignoring all the other events. When he did fly, he always landed beside his hangar as he had sprained his ankle, and avoided hobbling across the uneven turf. While all the other events were being contested Curtiss lounged outside his hangar in a deck chair.

The Gordon Bennett event was set up with the stipulation that the contestants should first make speed-trial flights. On the day of the race flying conditions were made hazardous by a sudden heat wave that caused many unpleasant turbulences. In their trial flights before the main event, Latham and Lefebvre turned in very poor times, owing to the flying conditions. G. B. Cockburn, the only British entry, could do only 38½ miles per hour, and withdrew when all trials were completed and the committee decided that only Blériot and Curtiss would be permitted to compete for the premier prize. In the trial flights Curtiss had flown at a speed of 51 miles per hour, and Blériot, trying one model after another, finally decided on his Number 22, powered with a 60-horsepower E.N.V. engine that apparently had beaten that mark, but when the chips were down and the prize flights started, neither pilot was able to reach 50 miles per hour. When the final figures were tabulated Curtiss had beaten Blériot by six seconds, and had won the world's first all-out speed contest with a mark of 46½ miles per hour.

In a later event, the Heidsieck Monopole and Roederer prize for the fastest three laps, Blériot had a chance for a victory over the American, but after taking off, a fuel line snapped and his machine caught fire. Blériot was just able to make a hurried landing, and clamber out with a badly burned arm and scorched face. Curtiss had no trouble in flying three faultless laps to take his second prize of the meet.

Aviation Meets Galore

The Reims competitions had proved that the aeroplane was here to stay and that people would pay for the privilege of sitting in grandstands to watch these man-made birds in action. Soon similiar events were announced at Antwerp, Berlin, Brescia (Italy), Frankfurt, Nice, Blackpool and Doncaster (England).

In fact, before the Reims meet was over, the mayor, the borough surveyor, and the advertising manager of the Blackpool Corporation were darting about the hangars signing up pilots to appear at a flying meet they planned to stage at the famous Lancashire seaside resort. Learning of their plan, Lord Northcliffe promised the full support of the *Daily Mail*. Realizing that they were fast coming into their own, the pilots made exorbitant demands for their appearances, but the British promotors willingly agreed. They had the names of Rougier, Paulhan, Leblanc, Latham, Fournier, Farman, and Fernandez on contracts before they left Reims.

By the time the Blackpool contingent arrived home, area rivalry developed, and, not to be outdone by Lancashire, Yorkshire immediately announced plans for an aviation meet to be staged at Doncaster, a manufacturing town that boasted the St. Leger racecourse, a most suitable place for such an event. Backing their town council to the hilt, the citizenry first signed Colonel Cody who had just made a cross-country flight of 47 miles. Cody was bound to a $10,000 contract, and given $2500 in advance, money which he badly needed, for by now he had been dropped by the British War Office. To back up the Cody name the Doncaster syndicate signed Delagrange, Le Blon, Sommer, and several lesser-known pilots.

This Blackpool-Doncaster rivalry gradually boiled up into a national joke in which *Punch* and leading newspapers played their parts to perfection. There were hilarious arguments as to which town could supply the finest overnight accommodations. Both factions were planning to greet at least 200,000 patrons. The railroads were drawn into the competition; their traffic managers found themselves advertising cutthroat, cut-rate excursions that threatened to bankrupt the lines. Every wild form of advertising was indulged in, and the Blackpool organization even printed a souvenir program in Esperanto, an artificial language.

The Royal Aero Club sanctioned the Blackpool meet, but

refused to recognize the Doncaster program. In rebuttal Doncaster's mayor insisted that nothing short of a blizzard would prevent them from staging England's *first* aviation meeting, and as if in answer to his challenge, the North Atlantic whipped up a hurricane, the tail of which flipped through both landing grounds. To cap the climax, *Punch* in the spirit of the discord announced: "All migratory birds that have not left our shores must take notice that flight will not be permitted on the days of the Blackpool flutter."

With so much widespread dissension seething, the newspapermen had to rent racing cars to dash from one shire to the other in order to keep up with the campaign.

At Doncaster, Colonel Cody lost an engine; one that had been shipped by truck from Aldershot. Four other British pilots arrived with monstrosities that couldn't possibly get off the ground. The syndicate that had arranged all the contracts quarreled with the Doncaster Town Council over the division of the profits, and before a propeller turned, they had taken the matter to the courts. So a receiver was appointed to take charge of all gate receipts.

In the meantime the rains came down. A brass band was prodded into action, and pumped out some dreary passages. A few people with turned-up collars and heavy boots appeared and sloshed about, peering into the worksheds. Several aeroplanes were drawn out for the photographers, and immediately became bogged in the mud. One suffered a broken fuselage and folded in the middle when the pilot climbed up to be photographed in the cockpit.

Colonel Cody, still stalking about in his sombrero and Inverness cape searching for his missing engine, had an unusual experience. On the second day, Sommer, Delagrange, and Léon Molon took to the air to familiarize themselves with the surrounding countryside as Cody looked on with interest. It was the first time he had watched an aeroplane in flight—he had never seen himself in the air. He was joined by Princess Victoria of Schleswig-Holstein, James J. Corbett, the American boxing champion, and others.

In an effort to add some interest to the dull proceedings, Cody took off in his monstrous *Cathedral,* and put on a fairly good show, but on landing piled up in a ditch that had been filled with nothing more substantial than furze cuttings. After downing a flask of brandy, the ex-cowboy ordered his wreck towed back to its shed where he spent the next three days rebuilding it.

Good Old Blackpool!

The Blackpool show was much better organized. Their Aviation Week, planned by men who had had years of experience in such matters, was enjoyed by spectators and contestants alike. Twenty-one pilots appeared, fourteen of them British, but not one British aircraft got off the ground. More than sixty thousand people turned out the opening day; not even the drenching, wind-blown rain could keep them away.

Louis Paulhan took off aboard a Farman in a light shower and made the first circuit of the program. H. Rougier took his Voisin up to 200 feet, and flew a one-mile circuit until his tank ran dry. Paulhan landed, refueled, and took off again with Henri Farman as a passenger. In the middle of this excitement, it was reported that the Count de Lambert had just flown over Paris and circled the Eiffel Tower at a height of 1200 feet. This news triggered the Blackpool officials to offer a prize for a flight around their own Blackpool Tower, a seaside replica of the Eiffel Tower, but the

Royal Aero Club committee refused to sanction such a feature, saying it was too dangerous.

The weather was still atrocious, but there was some reward in the refreshment tents where 38,000 dozen bottles of beer, a thousand cases of champagne, and a thousand hams were consumed.

Bored with sitting in his hotel waiting for good weather, Hubert Latham tore out to the field and ordered his frail *Antoinette* to be brought out. He arrived in the middle of a near gale and announced that he was going to fly, storm or no storm. Other pilots tried to dissuade him, but Hubert inserted another cigarette in his holder, and told his mechanic to swing the propeller. "These people bought tickets to see some flying," he pointed out. "Well, I'm going to show them some."

He did.

As he nosed out for his take-off a wild gust of wind lifted the *Antoinette* before it had run 10 yards. It was soon in the air, but under the storm conditions was flying backward. Experienced airmen scarcely dared to look as the monoplane swayed and tossed in the wild weather, but Henri Farman climbed up to the top of a pylon to get a better view. Latham fought the elements for more than 10 minutes, keeping his machine together, and once he had managed a turn, raced back over the course at a speed of better than 90 miles per hour. Out over the countryside he managed another turn, and then spent the next 10 minutes fighting his way back to the landing ground where he alighted during a short lull in the tempest. He put the *Antoinette* down in a perfect landing.

The whole, sodden crowd went wild, as Latham stood up in his cockpit, calmly removed his gloves and gave all credit to Levavasseur, designer of the aircraft. The Blackpool committee immediately awarded him a special prize of $1500. Henri Farman took $10,000 for winning the duration contest, while Rougier and Paulhan both pocketed worthy prizes for their efforts. From the point of view of flying, the Blackpool show was a dismal failure, for less than 200 miles had been flown, but the British public had had its first real taste of flying and wanted more. When the Lancashire show closed up, a great bulk of the patronage took a train for Doncaster where the committee had arranged to extend the program for two more days.

A change in the weather made flying comparatively simple. J. T. C. Moore-Brabazon won the *Daily Mail's* $5000 prize for a mile flight by a British aeroplane. This was flown aboard a Wright biplane that had been built by the Short brothers. Colonel Cody put on a theatrical act of being sworn in as a British subject before a grandstand full of spectators while a local band attempted to play *The Star-Spangled Banner*. Hubert Le Blon, after flying 22 miles in a rising gale, tried to return and land, but the wind tossed him about until it seemed he must settle amid the great crowd in front of the grandstand. At this point Le Blon won the questionable honor of being the first pilot in history to risk his life deliberately in order to save the lives of people on the ground. When it seemed that he must flop into the seething mass, he switched on his engine, jerked his Blériot up into a fluttering climb and slithered back on his tail to land behind the grandstand, a total wreck. The pilot suffered a few cuts and bruises, but no spectators were injured.

The band broke out with *Ach, du liebe Augustin,* and Le Blon was carried shoulder-high by a dozen newspapermen through the crowds of cheering spectators. Six months later he was killed at the San Sebastián aviation meet.

The Great Manchester Race

It will be recalled that in November 1906 Lord North-cliffe's *Daily Mail* had offered a prize of £10,000 (about $50,000 at the time) for a flight from London to Manchester. Amazingly, no one made an attempt to pick up this bonanza until April 1910, almost four years later. At that time, a little-known Englishman, Claude Grahame-White, filed an official entry. His effort was to provide one of the most interesting flying stories of that year.

By far the most colorful of all British aviators of this period, Grahame-White was born to fairly well-to-do parents. He went to school in Bedford, studied motor engineering, and in fact owned and drove one of the first motorcars seen in Great Britain. He became interested in aviation in 1909 and at the Reims exhibition that year he met Louis Blériot. He was so interested, he begged Blériot to let him buy one of his big two-seater machines, and watch it being built in Blériot's workshop. After some consideration it was agreed that Grahame-White should join the force as a common workman and clock in at six o'clock in the morning just the same as the rest of the working staff.

The new monoplane, christened the *White Eagle* was ready for its first test flight by November 1909, and was taken to the Issy-les-Moulineaux grounds. Blériot was at Vienna at the time and was not on hand to start the impatient Englishman's training, so Grahame-White decided to teach himself. With his friend Captain Fleetwood Wilson as a co-conspirator, they visited the field at early dawn to take the new machine out for some taxiing trials. Grahame-White had been advised that once the engine had been started, it would require at least six men to hold an aeroplane of this power, so the two conspirators lashed the tail of the Blériot to a fence. The big 60-horsepower engine started with the first try and Grahame-White scrambled up into the seat while Wilson untied the anchor rope. In seconds they were roaring across the field at 40 miles per hour.

This game continued for about twenty minutes, as they raced back and forth over the smooth turf, but Grahame-White soon tired of it and decided to risk an actual flight. Captain Wilson refused to be grounded, trusting that his friend would learn very quickly. The Englishman copied everything he had seen other aviators do, and went skimming over the field, and then made an acceptable landing. When the mechanics finally arrived, they were surprised to see Grahame-White aloft, flying speed circuits with the dash and daring of a professional.

When Blériot heard of this escapade, he ordered the *White Eagle* to be shipped to Pau where there was more room, and he himself hurried back from Vienna to conduct further trials there. At Pau the big monoplane proved to be faulty in design, and with Claude as his passenger, Blériot crashed into a wood, wrecking the machine beyond repair, so he gave Grahame-White two of his *Blériot* XIs, the cross-Channel model. The new owner soon gained his Aéro Club de France pilot's certificate with one of these and then boldly opened his own flying school in Pau. He ran this service with considerable success, until he remembered Lord Northcliffe's London-to-Manchester prize—he could use that money. But the little Blériots were incapable of long-distance cross-country flights, so he negotiated for a Henri Farman biplane.

He mastered this big machine in a short time, but Farman thought that he was not sufficiently experienced to attempt the London-to-Manchester test. To prove his point, Grahame-White took his mother aloft for more than an hour, finally satisfying Farman that he was quite capable of handling the biplane. The Farman was then packed in a crate and shipped to London. When the machine arrived in England, Grahame-White sent in his formal entry for the *Daily Mail* prize to the Royal Aero Club. Most of the other airmen who were capable of the same flight were taking part in a meet being staged at Nice, and enjoying the balmy Mediterranean spring for it was now well into April of 1910.

The Englishman planned his flight well by making a tour over the tracks of the London & Northwestern Railway in a special train, and selected two fields outside Rugby and Crewe as refueling bases. He arranged with the railway officials to have the sleepers (ties) at all junctions whitewashed to indicate the route to Manchester as he intended to use the gleaming rails as his course markers.

Grahame-White also planned to fulfill all requirements by taking off from a public park at Wormwood Scrubs, which was within five miles of the *Daily Mail* offices, but the London County Council's Park Committee withheld their permission, so the resourceful airman selected a strip of turf at Park Royal although it lay outside the five-mile limitation of the prize. He therefore arranged to fly from there to London and then set a course north for Manchester.

Once all the planning and the required arrangements had been completed, the aeroplane was taken from its crate and assembled for flying. Seeing the publicity value of the whole show, Henri Farman came over from Paris with one of his mechanics to take over the servicing of the aircraft. By midnight of April 21 the machine was ready, and all that was needed was a stretch of good weather and daylight for a take-off. However, the conditions were so inclement, less than a hundred people were on hand when the Englishman made his first start.

Always a dapper dresser, Grahame-White wore a neat khaki flying suit that he had designed himself. The ubiquitous Harry Harper had a powerful Darracq motorcar standing by to follow Grahame-White, and Claude's mother and sister appeared in the early morning frost to provide a small flask of brandy which he tucked in his pocket. His mother, unlike most parents who would have been fearful of such an exploit, warned, "Now do be careful, Claude, and please don't fly too low." Her son dutifully promised, and at 5:12 A.M. on April 23, Farman swung the prop and Grahame-White made a perfect take-off through the mist and swirling vapors and headed for the business section of London.

Workmen and shopgirls hurrying through the grimy streets of North Kensington stared up in wonderment as the aeroplane suddenly appeared overhead. An Aero Club official waved a white flag from the top of a gasometer on Kensal Rise, confirming the regulation start of the flight. The Farman pilot circled the gasworks once and then headed for Willesden Junction where he picked up the maze of railroad lines. By this time special editions of all London newspapers were flashing off the presses. The great flight was on. Manchester was 185 miles away. The drama began to unfold.

Once he had negotiated the bridges, telegraph wires, and signal stanchions marking Willesden, Grahame-White finally picked up his guide lines and settled down. News of his progress was flashed from signal box to signal box, and the muffled-up pilot waved to figures working along the road-bed as he proceeded at a roaring 40 miles per hour. He climbed to 150 feet where the temperature dropped. Sitting out on the leading edge of the lower wing with no shelter of any kind he soon was stiff with the cold, so he opened his flask and took a few sips of brandy. Feeling somewhat more comfortable, he found himself over the Buckingham-shire town of Bletchley where he had a moment of panic when his gleaming guide line vanished. Then he remem-bered that in this area the tracks went through a railroad tunnel, but he picked them again and continued on until he reached Rugby. By seven o'clock he was circling the field marked with white bedsheets. He landed, and the Darracq was already there along with Henri Farman, Perrin, and other mechanics to greet him. Their automobiles had beaten the aeroplane by many minutes.

Grahame-White was almost exhausted with the cold and strain of the flight and had to be helped down from his seat. The owner of the field warmed his hands in her muff. Someone poured a mug of coffee, and another friend wrapped the pilot in a fur coat and marched him up and down to bring back circulation to his stiff limbs. Then he was taken to a nearby cottage where he completely thawed out before an open fire. Meanwhile the mechanics refueled the Farman for the next leg to Crewe.

At 8:00 A.M. Grahame-White was circling the Rugby sta-tion, seeking his whitewashed sleepers that would guide him on the way. Below tiny locomotives screeched their welcome, and engineers leaned far out of their cabs to wave to the young airman. All seemed to be going well until he reached the vicinity of Lichfield when the Gnome engine rattled violently. Grahame-White immediately diagnosed the trouble as a broken valve, and put the machine down on a narrow strip of turf near a railroad embankment, and hurried to a nearby signal box to advise his followers that he was down at Hademore Crossing. The word was flashed all along the line, checking the onrush of motorcars that were following the flight. They all turned back from the far side of Lichfield and found Claude enjoying breakfast at the George Hotel. It was found that in landing he had broken one skid of the landing gear, but it was thought that the engine and skid could be repaired in an hour or so.

But a high wind came up, putting a stop to all flying. The aeroplane was repaired, but had to remain there until the weather improved. By early afternoon the wind suddenly heightened and the machine, having been left unattended by the mechanics who had gone off for a meal, was caught in a sudden gust and whipped over on her back. This caused damage that could not be repaired there, so it was decided to haul the wreck back to London, rebuild the Farman, and start off again.

Before the machine was dismantled and packed up, news was received that two French pilots, Louis Paulhan and Emile Dubonnet, had filed entries for the London-to-Manchester contest, but Grahame-White cheerfully said, "Well, if they want to make a race of it, I'll do my darnedest to oblige. There's still time to hustle back to London, patch up the Farman, and start all over again. At least I have the advantage of knowing two-thirds of the course."

An Epic Contest

The son of the famous wine merchant, Emile Dubonnet was a very skilled airman who piloted a Tellier monoplane. On the second day after he learned to fly he made a 50-mile cross-country flight, and on April 23, the day of Grahame-White's flight, he flew over Paris after taking off from

Juvisy. It was this success that prompted him to file for the London-to-Manchester flight. But the prize had been won before he could ship his monoplane from France to London.

Louis Paulhan had practically taught himself to fly, and had competed in the Reims meet, after which he was induced to appear in the United States where he made an altitude flight of 4500 feet at Los Angeles. He now had graduated to the Farman type, and on an impulse entered the *Daily Mail* competition.

While Grahame-White's machine was being dismantled in preparation for shipment back to London, his mother and sister who had followed him in Harper's Darracq, attended a church service at St. Mary's in Lichfield where for the first time the well-known Litany was lengthened to include aviators—"for those who travel by land, or sea, or in the air."

Aboard the train speeding back to London, Grahame-White read the newspapers. He was not particularly concerned with Dubonnet's entry, but he knew that in Paulhan he had an adversary of rare caliber. However, as soon as he learned that the twenty-six-year-old Frenchman was already at the Hyde Park Hotel, he sent him a wire of greeting: I WISH YOU BETTER LUCK THAN I HAVE JUST EXPERIENCED. STILL HOPE TO GET MY AEROPLANE REPAIRED AND READY TO MAKE A SPORTING CONTEST WITH YOU.

In similar spirit, Paulhan wired back: THANK YOU FOR YOUR GOOD WISHES. I HOPE WE GET TO MANCHESTER TO-GETHER.

The press had a rare holiday. Paulhan provided amusing copy, and his pretty wife was besieged as she shopped in London's fashionable stores. For a time Grahame-White was abandoned, but he finally persuaded the Parks Committee to permit him to use the Wormwood Scrubs field for his second attempt. Henri Farman had left him to give his aid to the Frenchman, although as a designer of the competing aircraft he might have taken an impartial stand. Patriotism had led him back to Paulhan. He argued, and perhaps rightfully, that Grahame-White had had his chance and had failed, although his ill luck was due chiefly to the neglect of the Farman mechanics to peg down the aircraft after it had been repaired at Hademore Crossing.

Paulhan had selected Hendon for his base of operations, a field that in later days became Grahame-White's London Aerodrome, scene of many important aviation events. During World War I it was acquired by the Air Ministry and named Hendon Aerodrome, and became a Defense of Britain fighter station and base for memorable Royal Air Force pageants during the inter-war years.

Activity on both fields actually began on April 26, 1910. Paulhan's Farman was a newer model than Grahame-White's, having a lower wing of shorter span that may have given it more speed. It was soon assembled and tested by the Farman team while Grahame-White was having to collect a scratch crew of workers who were fabricating new parts out of anything available, and working under the spluttery glare of naphtha flares. At odd minutes they took catnaps under the wings, on the hangar floor.

At 11:00 A.M., April 27, Grahame-White's Farman was ready for testing, but when the machine was dragged from its hangar there was a large crowd on hand that threatened to overrun the operation, and Claude was forced to climb aboard the plane and bellow through a megaphone, "Will you please clear off? I must have take-off space. You must move out of the way unless you want the Frenchman to win."

But the mob would not budge, and police reinforcements

had to be called out. Although good-natured and enthusiastic, the crowd simply would not be moved, not even by threats of being run over by motorcars, and Claude had to be content with a simple engine test of the Gnome rotary. It was impossible to make a flight test. Only a period of gusty rain dispersed the crowd, but flying was then impossible. To kill time Grahame-White drove to Hendon and found Paulhan sitting under a wing of his biplane, calmly contemplating the dour English weather. When these conditions continued, the Englishman decided to go to bed in a hotel at Wormwood Scrubs, but the Frenchman elected to sit it out, refusing to leave his base.

Shortly before 4:00 P.M. a break appeared in the weather, and Paulhan, deciding to stand by, sent a message to Grahame-White warning him that if the change continued, he would take off. For some reason this message was never delivered, and the Englishman slept on, unaware that Paulhan was preparing to start.

At 5:10 P.M. Paulhan kissed his wife goodbye, and climbed aboard. He made a beautiful take-off, circled the field twice and set off for the Hampstead cemetery which was within the five-mile mark of the *Daily Mail* offices. From there he headed for Willesden Junction and picked up a train he had hired to act as his guide and service base. It was not until a friend drove up to Grahame-White's hangar with the news that Paulhan had started that the English camp knew what was going on.

Grahame-White was soon aroused, and grumbled, "Well, if Paulhan's willing to break his neck, I'll damn well risk mine too."

"But the wind is much too high," his friends pleaded. "Surely you'll make a trial flight before starting off."

But the Englishman would not be denied. At 6:32 P.M.

(seventy-one minutes after Paulhan) he was in the air and racing after the Frenchman. The world's first cross-country race was under way and all of Great Britain went mad. Unquestionably, this amazing exhibition finally sold aviation to the country, and may have planted the seed that blossomed into the indomitable Royal Flying Corps a few years later.

Grahame-White's Farman biplane disappeared into the sunset and purple haze of dusk, as he tried his best to catch the flying Frenchman. Obviously, both men intended to fly until darkness forced them to land. Enjoying more than an hour's lead, Paulhan thundered on above his special train, as crowds gathered along all the roads to scream their enthusiasm. Signalmen again flashed the word along the line as they watched the faint glow from his engine's exhaust.

Once Grahame-White was airborne, whole fleets of cars took up the chase. Great crowds stood in front of the newspaper offices to read the bulletins. Lantern slides presented details of the race at motion picture theaters. By the time he reached Watford, Grahame-White had gained 11 minutes on Paulhan, and at Bletchley it was reported that he had picked up ten more. The same wild scenes were being enacted in Paris. A gigantic map was set up in the Place de l'Opéra, and model aircraft were used to show the relative positions of the contestants. Ruling heads of Europe were advised of the progress of the race. The world had not experienced such a contest before.

Passing Rugby, Paulhan dropped a weighted package from his machine that bore a note to his wife explaining that he intended to fly until he no longer could see the railroad lines. At 8:10 he landed in a field outside Lichfield, and his special train pulled up on a railroad embankment nearby to service his biplane. He had flown 117 of the 185 miles between London and Manchester. He explained that the flight was very cold and that he had flown through a rain shower, but he was determined to keep on.

Grahame-White was forced down by the fading light at 8:05 near the village of Roade, still some 57 miles behind Paulhan. A signalman invited him in for a mug of hot tea. Villagers helped him to stake down his machine, and a local doctor took him home to share his dinner.

By midnight, realizing that Paulhan would have an easy time covering his remaining 68 miles once the sun rose again, Claude decided to risk starting in the darkness with the hope of overtaking Paulhan before he could get into the air again. Everyone thought such an effort would be suicidal. No one had attempted a cross-country flight at night before.

"Well, I shall have to be given the credit for trying," Claude argued.

Flight by Moonlight

He ordered his Farman dragged to the far end of the field, and suggested that all available automobiles turn on their lights to lay a temporary flare path. The instant the moon appeared, he opened up the Gnome engine and plunged headlong down the field. He cleared the railroad embankment with inches to spare, and turned north just as the moon slipped behind a cloud. In an effort to put his cockpit in order he caught his sleeve in the ignition switch which shut off the engine. Not knowing what had happened, but sensing he was gliding back to the ground in complete darkness, his instinct was to try the ignition switch, and the rotary picked up immediately, and none too soon.

His automobile cavalcade, now led by a Stanley Steamer,

tore along the road and for some miles Claude used its headlights as his guide, and in that manner finally found the railroad lines again and once more set his course for Manchester.

Paulhan was snug under the covers when he was aroused and told that Grahame-White had attempted the impossible—taking to the air in the darkness—and was reported to be somewhere near Rugby, putting him only 34 miles behind. So Paulhan took off with the first gleam of daylight, flying high and well on his way to Manchester. For a short spell both airmen were in the air at the same time, but when he had reached the Trent Valley, Grahame-White's luck deserted him again. Gusty winds threw his Farman about, and then its engine gradually lost power. There was no choice but to land, and he managed to get down in an open field near Polesworth where his road contingent found him hanging on to a wingtip, valiantly trying to prevent his machine from being blown over again.

Encountering the same weather conditions, but flying with greater skill and a background of long experience, Paulhan continued on and reached Manchester at 5:32 A.M. after 90 minutes of buffeting. He said that he would not repeat that flight for ten times the amount of the prize money. However, forty years later on the anniversary of the race, April 28, 1950, the *Daily Mail* invited Paulhan, then sixty-six years old, to repeat his historic journey in a Gloster *Meteor* jet. He had taken 4 hours and 18 minutes flying time in 1910; in 1950 the distance was covered in 28 minutes. "It was just like going for a stroll," the Frenchman remarked.

Thousands of Britishers had stayed up all night to greet the winner when he landed at Didsbury, among them a young engineering apprentice, John Alcock, who nine short years later became the first man to fly an aeroplane nonstop across the Atlantic—from Newfoundland to Ireland.

The news of Paulhan's progress was flashed along the railroad system by the signalmen, and Grahame-White was among the first to learn that his rival had arrived safely.

"Well," he said philosophically, "as I have never had ten thousand pounds, I don't know what I have missed." He turned to look over the small crowd that had gathered, and added, "Three cheers for Paulhan! Paulhan's got there. He's the greatest aviator the world has ever seen. I am only a novice."

The three cheers were given with true sincerity.

At a special luncheon at the Savoy Hotel in London Paulhan was given a golden casket containing the £10,000, and Grahame-White was awarded a handsome silver consolation cup and a special gold medal of the British Aerial League.

Paulhan had won, but the race finally had made Great Britain air-minded. The two airmen had proved that flying was no longer a cheap sport, but could become a practical means of transport, and the aeroplane a machine of unbounded possibilities.

CHAPTER VIII

The Great Expansion

A Dangerous Sport • International Discord • Heroes of the Headlines • The Grand Circuits • The Paris–Rome–Turin Classic • Another Roman Holiday • A Man Named Weymann • For Honor and Glory • The Royal Flying Corps Is Formed • Hap Arnold's Aerial Hoax • The Golden Years

---

The headlined air races and aviation meets at which the world's leading pilots gave sensational performances were the prime causes of a great era of aviation expansion. The days of frantic experimental hops were ended, and dedicated men of all leading nations were learning to fly; even the Chinese had taken up the new science. Aircraft no longer were being built one by one in disused stables, abandoned workshops, or under tents, as men of finance were showing more than passing interest, and coming to the aid of the mechanical geniuses. By 1911 the full development of the aerial age was in the hands of the international bankers and high priests of Wall Street.

The long-drawn-out patent litigation between the Wrights and Glenn Curtiss attracted financial support to both sides. As explained, the Dayton mechanics were backed by men like Belmont, Vanderbilt, Gould, Shonts, and others of that standing. Curtiss also was able to get the support of men of equal stature.

In Europe, the Krupps, Hugo Stinnes, and other leading bankers of Germany, France, and Great Britain were backing aeronautical concerns, for by 1910 all were convinced of the practicality of navigation by air. Then, as though to add further testimony, Glenn Curtiss made his historic flight from Albany to New York, Charles Rolls completed a nonstop round-trip flight over the English Channel, and in another category the first commercial voyage of a Zeppelin, carrying thirty-two passengers, was made on June 22, 1910, between Friedrichshafen and Düsseldorf, a distance of 300 miles.

Aviation was the chief topic everywhere, and the Harvard Aeronautical Society, aroused by the interest in organized meets abroad, scheduled a program of flying to be staged at Boston during September. A total sum of $100,000 in prizes was put up, and popular fliers representing Great Britain and the United States were signed to appear.

Meanwhile, in July a British syndicate held a meet at Bournemouth which starred Léon Morane of France, J. Armstrong Drexel of the United States, and the now-famous Claude Grahame-White of England. The Frenchman won the top prize of $4000 for his flight from Bournemouth, out over the "Needles," three sharp, rocky projections off the westernmost promontory of the Isle of Wight, and back; a flight of 21 miles in all, 18 of which were over water. He covered the distance in 25 minutes, 12⅖ seconds. Drexel was second, and Grahame-White third. Morane also won the altitude flight by soaring to 4107 feet. Also at this meet another Frenchman, Emile Audemars, performed in one of Santos-Dumont's *Demoiselle* monoplanes, a tiny machine in which the pilot sat on a seat fitted to the undercarriage. This entry was dubbed the "Infuriated Grasshopper."

The Harvard Aeronautical Society's show, held at Squantum on Boston Harbor from September 3–13 in glorious weather, was a financial, social, and scientific success. It attracted celebrities from Boston, New York, and Washington, D.C.; even the President of the United States, William Howard Taft, was on hand to award the prizes. The pilots competing included Earle Ovington, Glenn Curtiss, Walter Brookins, Charles F. Willard, Ralph Johnstone, and Clifford B. Harmon. England sent Claude Grahame-White, T. O. M. Sopwith, and A. V. Roe.

Grahame-White won the big prize in the race around Boston Light, pocketing the Boston *Globe's* $10,000 check. He covered the 33 miles of over-water flying in 34 minutes, 1⅕ seconds. Aboard the same Blériot he also won the speed prize with a mark of 5¼ miles in 6 minutes.

Ralph Johnstone set the meet's endurance record with a flight of 3 hours, 5 minutes, and Brookins took the altitude prize with a climb of 4732 feet. Johnstone and Brookins flew Wright biplanes. Curtiss competed with a biplane of his own design, probably the same machine he had flown at Reims, but on this occasion it was not as fast as Grahame-White's Blériot.

A few weeks after the Boston meet, ex-President Theodore Roosevelt appeared at a show held at St. Louis, and on October 11 went aloft there in a Wright biplane that was flown by Archie Hoxsey, thus becoming the first former chief executive of the United States to fly aboard an aeroplane.

Maurice Tabuteau, a Frenchman, came into prominence with a flight over the Pyrénées when he took off on September 28, 1910, from San Sebastián, Spain, and flew to Biarritz, France, where he landed on a public square. This same Tabuteau was hired later by Sir George White who had set up an aircraft factory at Bristol, England, a venture that became the famous British and Colonial Aeroplane Company where all World War I aircraft, bearing the prefix "Bristol," were designed and produced. Tabuteau headed a pilot-training staff that taught many future Royal Flying Corps pilots how to fly.

Before the year 1910 was out, Claude Grahame-White staged another of his thrillers, this time right in the center of Washington, D.C., when on October 14 he piloted a Farman biplane from the old Bennings race track, circled the Capitol dome, and then landed in the street between the State, War, and Navy buildings, and the White House office building where he was greeted by thousands. He explained that he had come to return the call made by President Taft who had appeared at the Boston meet, but the President was out of Washington, so the hero of Manila Bay, Admiral George Dewey, rose to the occasion and did the honors by taking the Britisher to lunch at the Metropolitan Club, after which Grahame-White returned to his Farman and flew back to Bennings where he cracked up on its broad turfed area. A short while after he took off in his high-power Blériot monoplane, one that he had planned to fly in the second Gordon Bennett event, scheduled for two weeks later at Belmont Park in Long Island. This aircraft was also wrecked, which raises some query concerning the potency of the luncheon in Washington.

A *Dangerous Sport*

The Belmont Park program gave most New Yorkers their first experience of exhibition flying. The top feature possibly was the second Gordon Bennett contest, though a more spectacular feature was a prize of $10,000 for a speed event, starting from the racecourse, and winging out to the Statue of Liberty, and back.

This Statue of Liberty race will be long remembered. The event itself presented many hazardous factors as the line of flight was drawn over much of built-up Brooklyn, to say nothing of the conditions over lower New York harbor. In fact, Wilbur Wright forbade all of his pilots to take part in this event. No American insurance company would cover the Belmont Park authorities for liability—it was still widely believed that flying was a highly dangerous sport—but Lloyd's of London issued a $500,000 policy for a premium of $2500.

The conditions and terms of the second Gordon Bennett contest were more stringent than those applied to the event flown at Reims the year before. At Belmont Park the contestants were required to fly twenty laps over a 5-kilometer circuit, and it was stipulated that all take-offs must be made 1½ hours before sunset. In fact, Britain's James Radley who started 25 seconds late, was disqualified. This point was to be brought up many times in the controversy that marked the Statue of Liberty race.

There were many first-class airmen on hand with reliable mounts, and the program provided several stirring spectacles for the patrons. The French had a particularly strong team in Hubert Latham with a 100-horsepower *Antoinette,* and Alfred Leblanc and Eugene Aubrun with new Blériots. Great Britain was represented by Claude Grahame-White, W. E. McCardle, and James Radley who flew Blériots. Alec Ogilvie, who invented the first air-speed indicator, flew a Short-Wright biplane built in Britain. The holder of the trophy, Glenn Curtiss, declined to enter this time, pointing out that he did not want to "make a monkey of myself," competing against such talent. But the United States was well represented by Armstrong Drexel, one of Grahame-White's first pupils who favored the Blériot, Charles K. Hamilton with a Curtiss biplane, and Walter Brookins, Archie Hoxsey, Frank Coffyn, and Alfred Le Chappele. Brookins was selected to fly the Wright *Baby*, the single-seater designed especially for racing.

The Gordon Bennett event was staged on October 28, 1910, and as expected, proved to be a thriller; only two pilots completed the required twenty laps, three others wound up in the hospital, and a dozen flaming headlines were splashed across the newspapers.

Grahame-White, flying a new Blériot, powered with a 14-cylindered, 100-horsepower Gnome, was first off the mark. This machine had been rushed across the Atlantic, and had arrived just in time to compete; there wasn't an opportunity to make a test flight.

The new aeroplane rose off the turf like an enraged dragonfly, passed over the white canvas marker, and began the long series of circuits. Walter Brookins, aboard the *Baby* followed him. He took off at a steep angle, and soon was heading for a pylon, holding to the 100-foot level. He seemed to be doubling the speed put on by Grahame-White, but before he could begin his first circuit, something went wrong and the little Wright biplane suddenly nosed down, cracking up in front of the grandstand. The machine was a total wreck, but before an ambulance could reach the spot, Brookins was seen to be worming his way out of the framework. He staggered for about 20 feet, before an attendant could restrain him.

"Are you hurt?" he was asked. "Anything broken?"

"Only my heart," the American pilot said with a wan smile.

While Wilbur Wright had the wreckage carted away, Hubert Latham, as dapper and jaunty as ever, climbed into his *Antoinette*, lighted a cigarette, and took off. He guided his sleek monoplane through fifteen perfect laps, flying very low while passing the pylons, and giving the crowd a tremendous thrill. Then a sudden, vagrant wind caught his machine and sent it drifting toward the racecourse clubhouse. For a minute it looked as though the French machine would slam into the packed crowd, but Latham coolly held her level, increased his flying speed until he dared to risk a sudden zoom, then at the last possible instant nosed up and just cleared the clubhouse. The effort prevented a grim tragedy, but the *Antoinette* stalled with the effort and spun into an empty paddock nearby. Latham climbed out, laughed, selected another cigarette, and walked away to watch Claude Grahame-White coming in to land.

The Englishman had completed the course in 61½ minutes, making an average speed of 61 miles per hour. He had made an excellent show, but on his fifteenth lap, he caught a whiff of heated metal and scorched oil, and because of his short acquaintance with the new engine, he feared for a minute or two that the machine was on fire. His dread proved to be a false alarm, so he went on to finish, believing that he had at least taken second place.

He knew that Leblanc, also flying a Blériot, had been making his circuits with the grace and speed of a chimney swift. Flying like a man possessed, the Frenchman had cut every pylon so close it was obvious that he had trimmed many seconds off Grahame-White's time, but as with Brookins and Latham, bad luck rode with him.

Moving into his twentieth and final lap, with the crowd screeching its acclaim, Leblanc streamed away to the southeast, heading for the pylon marking the first turn. Suddenly the cheers of the crowd were stifled as they saw the speeding Blériot start to make the bank, and then nose down. It twisted painfully, and headed for a telegraph pole. They could see the French pilot tugging at the controls, but the Blériot continued to dive toward the pole. However, Leblanc managed to sideslip a trifle so that only the wing caught the obstruction. The pilot was tossed clear and was seen to climb to his feet.

Back at the Blériot hangar stood two full cans of gasoline. The mechanics responsible for servicing Leblanc's machine had hurried the job, and Leblanc had taken off with a half empty tank that had run dry on the final lap.

International Discord

The 1910 Gordon Bennett event was the first important aviation prize to be won by Great Britain, but the thrill of the success was tempered to some extent by the fact that Grahame-White had flown a French aeroplane, powered with a French engine.

Then there was the long-disputed Statue of Liberty race that resulted in a period of international discord. The writer who saw part of this event clearly remembers the details.

The premier event was scheduled for October 30, and the rules were clear and specific that all take-offs were to be made *before 4:00 p.m.* This is the more interesting when it is remembered that in the Gordon Bennett race James Radley, who was flying for Great Britain, crossed the starting line 25 seconds after the stipulated 1½ hours before sunset, and was disqualified.

The Comte Jacques de Lesseps, flying his Blériot *La Scarabée,* was first off the mark. Three minutes later Grahame-White with a Blériot, double the power of *La Scarabée,* caught up with the Frenchman and rounded the harbor statue 65 seconds ahead of him. Both pilots landed back at Belmont Park almost simultaneously, and Grahame-White with the faster time was declared the provisional winner.

At this point a touch of chauvinism stained the display. The American, John B. Moisant, who had had bad luck and smashed up his own Blériot, ran to Leblanc's hangar and ordered the Blériot mechanics on duty to haul out the reserve aircraft. The mechanics refused, saying that the machine belonged to M. Leblanc.

"You get that machine out of here," Moisant insisted. "It will be mine within twenty minutes." He and his brother who was at the meet with him hurried to a telephone and called Leblanc who was resting at the Knickerbocker Hotel in New York. Moisant's brother, a wealthy banker, offered Leblanc $10,000 for his reserve Blériot, and knowing that the machine was worth only half that amount, Leblanc agreed.

In the space of a few minutes John Moisant's numbers and colors were affixed to the Blériot. It was now past four o'clock, but Moisant took off and headed for the Statue of Liberty, and returned, bettering Grahame-White's mark by 43 seconds. When the British pilot protested and pointed out that Radley had been disqualified, the committee members blandly explained that the rules had been changed at the last minute to allow anyone to compete up to 5:00 P.M. When the British pilot demanded the clearance for a second flight, he was refused.

For a number of years this unfortunate situation was complicated further when it was announced in a few aviation journals that the Statue of Liberty race had actually been won by the Comte de Lesseps, who, it will be remembered, had taken off first in the race but had been caught and beaten by Grahame-White. In this variation it was stated the Englishman had been disqualified for "fouling the initial pylon," which only can be taken to mean he had hit the Statue of Liberty.

Backed up by all the French airmen competing in the Belmont Park meet, Grahame-White laid his case before the Fédération Aéronautique Internationale, and after an investigation that dragged on for two years, his point was upheld, and he received the $10,000 prize with $600 in accrued interest.

Before this meet was over Ralph Johnstone had shattered the world's record for altitude by flying to a height of 9714 feet.

Hurrying from the Belmont Park track Hubert Latham and Comte de Lesseps went to a meet being staged at Halethorpe in the Baltimore suburbs. The Baltimore *Sun* had contributed to the program by offering a prize of $5000 for a direct flight over that city. In those days few airmen risked passing over congested areas, but some of them had skimmed over outer suburbs, as a matter of necessity, rather than choice. The Comte de Lesseps made the first attempt, but bad weather forced him back. Before he could prepare for a second try Hubert Latham flew for more than an hour over the Maryland city, thrilling 500,000 people with his daring display. Again he used an *Antoinette* monoplane, and the date was November 7, 1910.

Heroes of the Headlines

Grahame-White and the rest of the British contingent took the next transatlantic liner home to take part in still another aviation thriller. Right after Blériot's Channel flight, Baron de Forest had put up a prize of $20,000 for the longest flight from Britain to the Continent by a British subject flying an all-British machine before December 31, 1910. No one had attempted to take this bonanza, because no British experimenter or manufacturer had produced as yet a machine capable of crossing the Channel and continuing on for any worthwhile distance.

But as the time began to run out, a few daring souls decided to make an effort, and as soon as they got back from the American meets, several Britishers congregated with their machines in the Dover area to await favorable weather. It was well into December before any of them made a deliberate move.

T. O. M. Sopwith and Cecil Grace were at Eastchurch with Short-built Wrights. Grahame-White, now flying a Bristol *Box-kite*, a copy of Farman's biplane, was at Dover, as were C. H. Greswell and Robert Loraine, the brilliant young star of the London theatre who was also an ardent airman. Alec Ogilvie had a camp on Camber Sands. Colonel Cody, with his slimmed-down *Cathedral*, planned to fly from Laffan's Plain, and Lieutenant H. E. Watkins of the Essex Regiment, who had learned to fly at Brooklands, waited at Shorncliffe with a Howard T. Wright, a pusher

with a monoplane tail. Once more, Great Britain was re-
galed with hourly headlines, and the promise of aerial
heroics.

After getting a good weather report from Harry Harper
who had access to such information, Sopwith took off from
Eastchurch on December 18 and swung out across the
Channel. No Royal Navy ships were available to escort him,
as the Admiralty in its best Gilbert and Sullivan tradition
had declined to join in, explaining that it was unwilling to
break up the Christmas leave program of its crews.

Grahame-White, who was determined to keep up his winning ways, first made a test flight with his new Bristol *Box-
kite* from Swingate Downs, but immediately on take-off he
was caught in a sudden gust, and carried dangerously close
to the edge of the cliff, where he crashed. Fortunately, he
was able to crawl from the wreckage with only a few cuts
and bruises that put him in bed for several days.

Meanwhile Sopwith had safely negotiated the Channel
and landed at the village of Beaumont, Belgium, covering
a distance of 177 miles. Villagers who had never seen an
aeroplane, displayed remarkable indifference when Sopwith
explained that he had just flown from England; they merely
asked him what the weather was like over there.

Assuming that such a modest hop would not be likely to
win Baron de Forest's prize, Sopwith hurried back to Dover
that night to learn if any of his rivals had bettered his mark,
in which case he would try again.

But it was four days later, December 22, before another
Briton took off. This time it was Cecil Grace in a Short-
Wright machine. He left from Eastchurch on the Isle of
Sheppey, having chartered a Dover tug to escort him half-
way across the Channel, and then detailed a second one
out of Calais to cover the rest of the over-water trip. Grace

made the crossing successfully, but tail winds on which he had relied to beat Sopwith's mark suddenly reversed and he landed at Les Baraques near Calais. He decided to go back to England and try again.

Having dismissed the tugs, he planned to use the cross-Channel packet *Pas de Calais* as his escort, but the boat train from Paris was late, delaying the steamer. After refueling, and impatient with waiting, Grace took off and, as mentioned before, was never heard of again.

More doleful news came out of the contest. Grahame-White had had his Bristol rebuilt but it never took to the air again. During a high wind his hangar collapsed and the *Box-kite* was wrecked once more. While trying out his Short-Wright on Camber Sands, Alec Ogilvie piled up and put himself out of the race. Robert Loraine, using a Bristol, wrecked his mount while test flying at Eastchurch. So the result of all this melancholy effort was that T. O. M. Sopwith received the prize of $20,000 for a flight of but 177 miles.

But before the year was out Colonel Cody won the British Empire Michelin trophy on December 31 with a flight of 189 miles in 4 hours, 47 minutes over Laffan's Plain. He received only $2500 but the money was more than welcome as he had had a lean year.

Cody had completely redesigned the big *Cathedral*, lightened it considerably, and after trying two 60-horsepower engines, finally decided to mount one centrally with a direct-drive propeller. He began the Michelin event with a flight of 94 miles over the closed circuit, and when Sopwith put on 107 miles, Cody tried again, raising the mark to 117 miles. Ogilvie then took the lead with 140 miles, and this effort stood for several days although both Sopwith and Cody tried manfully to beat it, but were handicapped by high winds. Finally, on the last day of the year, racing against Sopwith, Cody managed to stay in the air for 189 miles. Sopwith gave up after 150 miles, too cold and frozen to continue.

The Grand Circuits

In another effort to improve Britain's standing in the world of aviation Lord Northcliffe in the summer of 1910 offered another prize of £10,000 for a 1000-mile circuit of Britain, to be contested for in the summer of 1911. He felt that the industry needed improved aircraft and more skilled airmanship—not programs of spectacular flying. How much this was needed can be noted that by the end of 1910 France had 353 qualified pilots, England had only fifty-seven, and Germany forty-six. The United States could boast of only a handful.

French newspapers were quick to respond to Northcliffe's lead, and three more demanding circuits were added to the 1911 program, all of which were to precede the British competition.

The first big event was the Paris-Madrid race, a test of 874 miles to be flown in three stages: Paris–Angoulême–San Sebastián–Madrid. Twenty-eight pilots were entered, eight of whom were French Army officers who however were ordered not to fly across the Spanish frontier. There were nineteen monoplanes, and only nine biplanes. No British or American pilots or aircraft were entered.

The keen rivalry displayed in this contest perhaps could be traced to the fact that important military contracts were pending. The competition among the French aircraft firms promised to be lively. In this event two new, but most colorful Frenchmen, were listed as the favorites. The first was Jules Védrines, a professional mechanic and a sensational Blériot pilot who became one of France's heroic airmen in the early months of World War I. He flew under contract to the Morane company for this competition. The second was Roland Garros, concert pianist, who had been taught to fly by Santos-Dumont, and who was to devise the first fighter aeroplane in which a fixed machine gun fired through the revolving blades of the propeller. A third pilot of some note was Lieutenant Jean Conneau of the French Navy who flew under the *nom d'air* of André Beaumont, because he had reverted temporarily to civilian status for this event. Conneau was one of the first experts in aerial navigation, disdaining the general rule of following familiar landmarks, roads, railroads, etc. Before each flight he drew an accurate course, allowing for winds and details of the latest weather reports, after which he climbed to a comfortable altitude and flew by map and compass.

The start of the Paris—Madrid race was slated for May 21, 1911, from the Issy-les-Moulineaux airfield. The French Premier, Ernest Monis; the Minister of War, Henri Berteaux; and dozens of high government officials were on hand to witness the occasion, as well as thousands of people who had camped out all night. Hundreds of police could not handle the crowds, and when Védrines attempted to take off in a Morane at 5:00 A.M., he was forced to ground-loop to prevent an accident, and was tossed out of the speeding machine. It looked for a time as if the ex-mechanic was out of the race.

The other pilots took off one by one. The fifth was E. Train, inventor of the Train monoplane, who carried a passenger. He managed to get away despite the surging crowds, but after making a turn to pass by the distinguished visitor's stand, his engine cut out, and seeing swarms of people still cluttering the field, he swung toward the stands and smashed into the group of government officials. M. Berteaux was killed instantly, his right arm severed by the propeller. The Premier, Ernest Monis, was badly injured about the head and face, and in the ensuing panic more than fifty others were seriously injured.

After grave consideration, the promoters decided to call off the Paris–Madrid race, but the injured Monis insisted that it be continued, so all starters were called back, and a new take-off arranged for the next day. By this time Védrines had a new Morane, and he got away safely, being the first man to reach Angoulême. Conneau had engine trouble when he was about 126 miles from Paris, and had to make a forced landing that shattered his propeller. On the Angoulême–San Sebastián leg all but three of the contestants were eliminated. Machines were scattered all over Gascony. Only Roland Garros, Eugene Gilbert, and Jules Védrines were left, with Védrines well in the lead, having beaten the crack *Sud-Exprès* by five hours, which shows how these races were increasing the speeds of the aeroplane. Only a year before Grahame-White had been unable to keep up with his service train during the London-to-Manchester race.

Madrid was still 343 miles away, and the course now vaulted over the Pyrénées, and the Sierra de Guadarrama, but Védrines was positive he could make it in one hop. He took off during a blazing hot day and, because he flew without a cap or helmet, almost suffered a sunstroke. Then, on reaching the Pyrénées the air was rougher than anything he had encountered before, and for a long while he was in great danger of being dashed to the deep ravines below. There were many turbulent heat drafts to contend with, and wild vortexes swirled off the jagged peaks, or roared along the narrow valleys. As though this were not enough, Védrines was attacked by a darting eagle that swooped at the little monoplane, attempting to claw the pilot's head with its talons, and screeching its wrath. Someone had given Jules a small revolver, and he tried shooting at his attacker. He emptied the chamber, and whether he hit the bird or not he did not know, but the big eagle finally turned away.

But this was not the full catalogue of Védrines tribulations. A valve spring of his Gnome engine broke, and he had to force-land at Burgos, Spain.

Following in wild chase, Gilbert was forced down in Navarre, and spent hours scouring the countryside for a few tools, while Garros piled up 14 miles outside San Sebastián. The field was open for Védrines, and early the next morning he arrived at Madrid where King Alfonso was on hand to greet him, and to set up a week-long display of Spanish hospitality.

The Paris–Rome–Turin Classic

But all good things must come to an end, and awash with Spanish wines and omelets, Védrines returned to France to enter the Paris–Rome–Turin race. He was about a week late, but the rules stated that competing pilots could take off from Paris on any day within two weeks from the formal start, and the pilot completing the distance in the shortest aggregate flying time was to win the $60,000 prize. What a bonanza exhibition-flying provided in those days!

The Paris–Rome–Turin classic (?) was sponsored by the French *Le Petit Journal,* and was one of the best-managed

Official U.S. Navy Photograph

5. In 1911 Lieutenant T. G. Ellyson of the U.S. Navy worked out a novel method of launching a flying boat. Starting from a 15-foot high platform he glided down a 250-foot wire cable fastened to a spike in Lake Keuka and took off successfully. This take-off had considerable bearing on the seaplane catapult soon to be adopted.

Imperial War Museum Photo

6. The monoplane that flew the English Channel also went to war in 1914, a reconnaissance machine. This Bleriot XI-2 was the equipment flown by one of Britain's air-squadrons during the early months of the war.

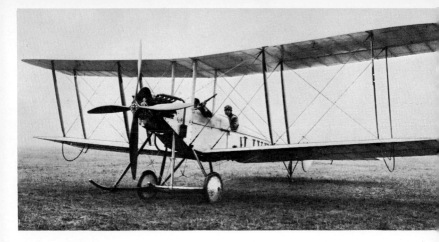

27. Full proof that the early warplanes were armed only with a rifle. He**
is an early B.E. 2c biplane showing the observer in the front seat aiming **
Lee-Enfield .303 rifle. This particular model was powered with a 90-hp RA**
engine which gave a speed of 72 mph.

28. In 1913 the Vickers company designed and produced this Experiment**
Fighting Biplane which had a Vickers gun mounted in the nose and two se**
of celluloid windows for visibility—and a higher fire hazard. However, th**
machine never went into production for active service. The F.B. 5 mod**
later became the famed Vickers Gunbus of 1915.

Imperial War Museum Photo

. The warbirds show their colors. Here is the first evidence of marking
arplanes for active service. These Bristol Scouts, wearing the Union Jack,
ere first seen on a Royal Naval Air Service field in France, late in 1914.
gain, note the lack of any armament.

Imperial War Museum Photo

. Louis Breguet, early in the field of aeronautics, was one of the first
renchmen to produce a satisfactory tractor biplane. Here is his 1912 model
mplete with tricycle landing gear, four-bladed prop and wheeled control
lumn. Note also the single interplane struts.

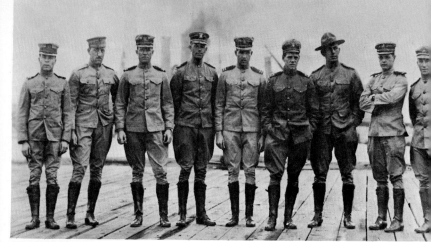

31. By March of 1914 the U.S. Navy had established a flying school at Pensacola, Florida. Among the commissioned officers taking the course that year were the above (left to right): Lieutenant V. D. Herbster, Lieutenant W. M. McIlvain, Lieutenant P. N. L. Bellinger, Lieutenant R. C. Saufley, Lieutenant J. H. Towers, Lieutenant Commander H. C. Mustin, Lieutenant (Army) B. L. Smith, Ensign de Chevalier and Ensign M. L. Stolz.

32. An early British attempt at flight-deck aviation. A Sopwith Camel pilot of the Royal Naval Air Service, in 1917 tried to land on a towed lighter but missed the tiny platform. In August of the following year Sub-Flight Lieutenant Stuart D. Culley took off from such a lighter and shot down the German Zepplin L.53 and scored the first flight-deck victory in air history.

contests of its kind. More than 250,000 attended the start at Buc aerodrome near Versailles where the new Minister of War, M. Goiron, was guest of honor. Twelve aeroplanes actually started, ten monoplanes, and two biplanes, but there were no British or American entries. As Védrines had not yet returned from Madrid, he was a problematical starter, leaving Conneau (André Beaumont), and Roland Garros the favorites.

Within half an hour of the start, Conneau and his Blériot were down in a wheatfield with a set of oiled-up spark plugs. After watching a number of other contestants pass over, the Navy lieutenant took out his holding-down ropes, lassoed a grazing horse, and rode bareback into the nearest town and bought a new set of plugs. He also recruited a number of men to help remove stooks (wheat sheaves) and clear a runway. Before this task was completed, another aeroplane in trouble used this temporary runway to land. This was too much for the villagers—two visiting aeroplanes in one day—so they shuffled off to the nearest *estaminet* to recount the historic events. Conneau had to finish the stook removal himself before he could take off again. But despite this delay the Navy lieutenant arrived at Dijon 19 minutes ahead of Garros. After lunching together, they both took off again, landing at Avignon before nightfall.

With the dawn next morning Garros and Conneau were airborne once more, heading for Nice. Again Conneau was in trouble when he battled for three hours with the vortexes and clouds of a Mediterranean mistral (a violent, cold, northeast wind). He finally gave up and landed at Brignoles, about 30 miles east of Marseilles.

Garros was no luckier. After a similar experience in the same storm, he crashed in the Rhône delta, and tore off both wings of the Blériot. But the concert pianist was not to be defeated. He appealed to the local police and they rushed him back to Avignon where he bought another aircraft owned by a local amateur pilot. The rules allowed such measures, particularly after the Moisant affair at Belmont Park. Taking off again, Garros flew south, heading after Conneau.

The naval flier was delayed for six hours at Brignoles, but finally took off for the next control, Fréjus, but was so exhausted on his arrival at 6:45 P.M. he had to be cared for by a doctor. He had about resolved to stay there overnight, when to his amazement he saw Garros appear over the horizon. Screaming to his mechanics to start his engine, Conneau jumped into the cockpit and took off again. He passed Cannes, flying a few miles out to sea, and he could see the welcoming lights of Nice when his engine started to cough and then conked out. Gliding down, he slipped into a bank of fog where the Gnome again picked up, and he was able to continue, and finally set down at Nice. Forty minutes later the redoubtable Garros joined him. The rest of the contestants were strewn out along the length of Provence (southeast France, east of the Rhône).

That night Nice went wild, and many fantastic wagers were made as to whether either pilot would reach Rome the next day. Neither did. When Conneau went out to his Blériot the next morning he was told by his mechanics that his engine had been put out of action with sand and water. The Gnome was damaged beyond repair, and he had to telegraph to Paris for a replacement. Whether this was ugly sabotage, paid for by cheap gamblers was not known, but Conneau had to stand by and watch Garros take off for Genoa.

Roland Garros did very well. He passed over Monte Carlo, crossed the Italian frontier at Ventimiglia, and was next reported over San Remo. He landed at Genoa in time for a late breakfast.

During the Conneau-Garros rivalry, Adolf Frey, a German contestant, had struggled on from Avignon to Nice where he paused only to refuel, and, watched by the frustrated Conneau, took off for Genoa. This information which was wired ahead, taunted Garros to get out of Genoa and head for Pisa, which he reached safely and spent the night there.

Once more the host town paid homage to the leader, wining and dining Garros. The following morning he took off for Rome and glory, but about 20 miles outside Pisa he cracked up again, wrecking his second Blériot. This time he telegraphed for a new machine and received Louis Blériot's assurance that one would be put aboard a chartered express train and rushed to him.

In the meantime, Frey who was physically exhausted, had forgotten to give his engine its customary overnight servicing, and it let him down just short of his Genoa goal.

Now the scene had shifted completely, and Conneau was alone once more, his route wide open. The Gnome officials had put a new engine in the back seat of a fast car and hired a noted racing driver to deliver it to Nice. It was installed in the Blériot overnight, and Conneau took off on the fourth day of the race, and with no trouble at all overtook Garros and Frey and continued on to Rome and victory.

Jacques Schneider, son of the founder of the Schneider-Creusot armament firm, helped Conneau to escape from the wild crowd that greeted him at Rome's Parioli airfield, and during this encounter it struck Schneider that it was paradoxical that a naval officer should be flying a land plane, and he conceived the idea of setting up an international race for seaplanes. But this plan did not completely flux until December 1912 when he announced publicly his donation of the famed Schneider Trophy, and its monetary prizes for a seaplane speed contest that was eventually won and permanently taken by the British.

Garros arrived in Rome the next day with his third Blériot. According to the rules he and Conneau should have remained there for a full week before heading for Turin, but because of the 1025-mile Circuit-of-Europe event next on the aviation calendar, they agreed mutually to forego that hop and consider the race finished.

Another Roman Holiday

The Circuit-of-Europe race was sponsored jointly by the Paris *Journal* and the London *Standard*. The promoters donated $100,000 in prize money and planned what they hoped would be the most sensational of all air races. It was. It resulted in the deaths of three pilots, and a fatal duel between two officials who had disagreed over the precise interpretation of the rules. The Circuit-of-Europe was a shockingly wanton, gladatorial spectacle.

In its plans it appeared to be just another city-to-city grind with no mountains or high-altitude hazards; most of the course stretched over low country (Paris – Liège – Spa – Utrecht – Brussels – Roubaix – Calais – Shoreham – London – Shoreham – Calais – Paris). The only hazard, if by now it could be so considered, was the double crossing of the English Channel.

The record prize money attracted sixty pilots to the Champ de Manoeuvre at Vincennes, the starting point, on June 18, 1911, but only nine finished. As was to be expected, the rivalry between Védrines and Conneau topped the accompanying stories for each man had won one classic race. Only two Englishmen, Jimmy Valentine in a Deperdussin, and Oscar Morison in a Morane had signed up. However, Sir George White had entered a Bristol *Box-kite* and hired Tabuteau to fly it. There were no American entrants.

The European circuit provided disaster and tragedy right from the start. Among the first to take off was Lieutenant F. Princeteau, a French military airman who had been instructing at the Blériot school at Hendon. He overturned his monoplane, and was trapped inside the wreckage for a short time. The fuel tank exploded and set him afire, and he was seen to scramble out, completely enveloped in flames. He died in frightful agony in front of the grandstand before aid could reach him.

A few minutes later T. Lemartin, military adviser to the Blériot Company, went out of control at 200 feet, crashed, and was killed outright. Another Blériot pilot, listed only as Gobert, piled up in front of the grandstand, losing one eye and both legs. Before the last contestant had left Vincennes, Landron who was flying a Pischoff, crashed and burned to death near Château Thierry, and the British pilot Morison had perched his Morane in the trees that fringed the airfield.

From this point on the Circuit-of-Europe furnished the usual spectacle of near tragedies and crack-ups. There was considerable dissension following that Sunday, June 18; the pilots arguing that they wished to fly in a race, not a catastrophe, and under ideal conditions. "We are sick of providing black headlines for the newspapers," said Maurice Tabuteau who flew the only biplane that completed the race.

But, paradoxically, eleven pilots crossed the Channel with no trouble within a period of 45 minutes, an interesting episode when one considers that Louis Blériot's "miraculous achievement" had been accomplished but two years before.

The Circuit-of-Europe dragged on for three weeks, but was won finally by Lieutenant Conneau who had taken the lead right from the start, due mainly to his accurate navigation. It seemed uncanny how he flew from one control to the next without losing his way; in practically all instances he appeared over the landing ground at exactly the time he had calculated. Védrines, who flew a more conservative race than usual, had to be content with fourth place.

A Man Named Weymann

Long missing from the winners' circle, American airmen received an encouraging fillip on June 1, 1911, when in its third competition the Gordon Bennett Trophy was brought back to the Aero Club of America by Charles T. Weymann, an almost unknown who had learned to fly in France. He was highly skilled in cross-country flying, and on September 7, 1910, had flown from Buc to Clermont-Ferrand, a distance of 231 miles with only three stops, and while carrying a passenger.

A small, dapper man, Weymann, who had been born in Haiti, always wore a scholarly pince-nez while flying. He had been taken under the wing of the Aero Club of America and provided with a Nieuport that was powered with a 14-cylindered, one hundred-horsepower Gnome engine. This machine had been built for the French Military Trials of 1911, and was a midwing monoplane, unquestionably the fastest mount available anywhere. The Nieuport firm had been established in 1910 by Edouard de Nieport, commonly called Nieuport. Later military versions of the Nieuport bi-planes had great success in World War I.

Flying over a 94-mile course at Eastchurch, Weymann won the international event with a speed of 78.77 miles per hour. He was the only American in the race and just nosed out Alec Ogilvie of England, and Edouard de Niéport and Alfred Leblanc of France. In fact, these four were the only ones to finish the race.

Three weeks later, July 22, 1911, the long-awaited Cir-cuit-of-Britain meet was staged, and proved to be one of the finest events in the history of aviation. For one thing, it provided a thrilling climax to the coronation celebrations for King George V, and its impact on the British public *and* British military authorities was all that Lord North-cliffe could wish.

The officials of the *Daily Mail* worked hand-in-glove with a committee from the Royal Aero Club, and all concerned were determined that the Circuit-of-Britain should not be another Roman holiday, but a well-planned test of both pi-lots and aircraft. The circuit covered 1010 miles and was more difficult than the Circuit-of-Europe, but everything possible was done to prohibit reckless flying, or the taking of unnecessary risks.

The course selected after the take-off from Brooklands was Hendon – Harrogate – Newcastle – Edinburg – Stir-ling – Paisley – Carlisle – Manchester – Bristol – Exeter – Salisbury Plain – Brighton – Brooklands. No substitution of aircraft was permitted, once the race had started, and five vital parts of each airframe as well as the engine were stamped; only three of these could be replaced during the race without penalty. More than 500,000 people watched the finish of the first leg at Hendon, and 100,000 left their beds at 2:00 A.M. to witness the take-off of the second day's flying. There was a $50,000 prize for the winner.

Thirty pilots had sent in entries, but only seventeen of them were actual starters. Charles T. Weymann, still with his Nieuport from the Gordon Bennett exhibition, was the only American in the race. Austria had Lieutenant H. Bier in an Etrich, the original Taube-type monoplane that was to be adopted by the German Air Service. Emile Audemars, a Swiss, entered with a Blériot, and the French contingent, headed by Lieutenant Conneau and Jules Védrines, included G. Blanchet and De Monthalant. Still flying under his *nom d'air*, André Beaumont, Conneau again flew a Blériot while Védrines stayed with his Morane. This time Great Britain was well represented, but mostly by newcomers. The list included H. J. D. Astley, Lieutenant R. A. Cammell, Gustav Hamel (who flew the first official airmail for Britain on September 9, 1911), B. C. Hucks, C. C. Paterson, H. Pixton, C. P. Pizey, Lieutenant H. H. P. Reynolds, and Jimmy Valentine. Claude Grahame-White was too busy running his flying school at Hendon. A. V. Roe was planning for military contracts with a triplane and a biplane. Only Colonel Cody with his cut-down *Cathedral* was on hand to represent the true pioneers of British aviation. Despite all this French and British opposition, Weymann with his racy Nieuport was the early favorite.

For Honor and Glory

The Circuit-of-Britain started from Brooklands at 3:00 P.M. on July 22, a Saturday. The first leg of 20 miles took the contestants to Hendon, where the foreign pilots were surprised to learn that there would be no flying the next day

—Sunday. Determined to cover their show from every point of vantage, the *Daily Mail* hired a fleet of twenty Ford cars and put two hundred local correspondents at all strategic points along the course.

The opening day provided a sizzling 90 degrees in the shade, but a large crowd was on hand, including Prince Henry of Prussia, Prince Charles of Rumania, King Manoel of Portugal, and the Gaekwar of Baroda. Amusingly enough, Lord and Lady Northcliffe, having forgotten to pick up their passes, were refused entrance for more than half an hour by a resolute gatekeeper who did not recognize the chief sponsor of the aerial event.

All contestants got safely away from Brooklands, but Weymann had to turn back after a splendid start. It seems that his map had blown away while he was making his take-off. The British Army pilot Lieutenant Cammell was forced down on Hounslow Heath with engine trouble, and had to withdraw.

The following day permitted the pilots to visit the London Hippodrome where they saw scenes of the start and finish of the first day's flight on the motion picture screen. This was considered something of a miracle as the films were developed and printed in three hours, a record for those days.

That Monday was long remembered in England. All stores were closed in Harrogate, and along the Tyneside, shipyards that were turning out vessels for the Royal Navy were strangely silent; the workmen had hurried to Newcastle to watch that portion of the race. Conneau, Védrines, Hamel, and Valentine were soon in the lead, but Hucks crashed just north of Luton. Audemars had engine trouble and had to quit. Bier came down at Hatfield with a leaking radiator. Pixton crashed at Spofforth. Pizey reached Melton

Mowbray and checked out because of engine trouble. Weymann lost his way, came down in rough country and buckled his undercarriage.

There was more trouble all along the line. De Monthalant also became lost and came down at Wetherby, calling it a race. Blanchet was out of the contest because of a faulty engine, and Astley in a Birdling machine was lost in a fog. He flew around Bedford four times before he found an open field. After landing he ate a late breakfast that disagreed with him, and shortly after he took off again, he had to come down.

In the meantime Védrines and Conneau were battling it out, with Védrines taking the lead early that morning as they reached Kettering. The control officials at Harrogate were expecting the first arrivals at 7:00 A.M., and the two Frenchmen were only 4½ minutes apart with Védrines still in the lead, flying with faultless navigation. After a quick inspection of his craft, Védrines was off again. Conneau took time out for a coffee well laced with cognac. Valentine was the first Britisher to reach Harrogate, but he was kept waiting there for an hour while a local delegation formally presented him with a silver tea service. Two hours after Valentine got away, Cody sailed in with his big propeller lazily batting the breeze. On landing, he explained that while over Rotherham a radiator tube had burst, and he had had to land to repair it, and with Harrogate in sight his gasoline tank had broken loose from its bracket.

Hamel who followed Cody in almost passed out when he climbed down from his cockpit, for he was still weak from an accident he suffered in the Gordon Bennett race. When someone told him that Védrines and Conneau were already in Edinburgh, he bellowed, "Oh, no! Then I must go on!"

He managed to reach the Scottish city, but had to give in to complete exhaustion.

It was true. Védrines was in Edinburgh, and Conneau was only 11 minutes behind him. Cody had remained at Harrogate to repair his fuel tank bracket. Valentine was only one hour behind Conneau. So far the weather had not been too bad, but that night rainstorms swept over the country, bringing an end to twenty-five days of drought. The greater part of the rest of the Circuit-of-Britain was flown under the worst of weather conditions.

Making the most of the early dawn, Védrines and Conneau took off at 3:00 A.M., and raced westward up the valley of the Forth, and by the time they reached Stirling, the heavens opened. Conneau went into the lead at the Paisley racecourse, a few miles west of Glasgow where a tremendous crowd from the Clydeside dockyards welcomed the airmen. Conneau, still flying by his own navigation system, said he had not seen the Clyde, nor spotted any part of Glasgow, but made Paisley by picking up the river after he had dropped from 900 to 600 feet. Fortunately there were no obstructions higher than 200 feet in the Edinburgh–Glasgow area.

While mechanics checked over his engine, Conneau sipped whisky from a flask. In a few minutes Védrines was heard above in the mist, circling for a view of the ground below, and before he could land, the French naval lieutenant was off again, heading southeast for Carlisle. Védrines continued to circle and circle still trying to find the racecourse. His service crew wrung their hands in despair as time after time they heard Jules passing just over their heads. They lit great bonfires, fired guns, and sounded their Klaxon horns, but Védrines continued to circle for nearly an hour before he found a hole, and landed. He stayed just long enough to gulp a cup of coffee and to be refueled.

Meanwhile Conneau had dared the crowning peaks of the Pennine Chain and floundered into Carlisle, just east of Solway Firth. A wild throng greeted him, but as he climbed down, their concerted cry died down to a low groan. The Frenchman was just able to throw his leg over the fuselage, clamber down, and steady himself against the edge of his wing. He was speechless, dazed, and for a minute staggered aimlessly, while rolling up his map. Finally he explained, "My engine . . . it was bad right from the start. I could see great blue hills in the distance, but my engine . . . it would not pull. But I knew Védrines would soon be after me. I did my best, but still she would not pull, and then the mountains were there not fifty feet below my wheels! I looked for a place to land, but there was nothing but great hills and deep valleys. There was nowhere to land . . . nothing. At one point I was caught in a 'pocket' and down I went. It was not flying, it was just like falling into nothing. I lost more than three hundred feet before there was any air that would support me. It was terrible."

While Conneau waited for some refreshment and refueling, Védrines, who had taken off from Paisley shortly after Conneau, was soon blanketed in clouds and could not see 30 feet in any direction. He was drenched with rain, pelted with hail, and buffeted about until he was sick as a dog and had to vomit over the side of his frail cockpit. But he managed to land at Carlisle 30 minutes after Conneau.

On the Manchester leg both pilots became hopelessly lost. Conneau dropped down at Settle, while Védrines had to land at St. Helens to inquire the way. After selecting a new course they both continued on, and eventually landed at Manchester. Conneau was first, and was so exhausted he fell asleep in some straw, but after 35 minutes was aroused by the hum of a Gnome engine. He leaped to his feet and took off for Bristol.

After a short rest, Védrines was in the air again chasing after his countryman, and by this time the whole of England was absorbed in the hourly reports of this historic contest. Only Védrines and Conneau were considered, although Hamel, Cody, and Valentine were still slogging on. Hamel was at Edinburgh, Cody at Newcastle, and Valentine had reached Carlisle.

Once Manchester was passed, the weather improved and Conneau reached Bristol 65 minutes ahead of his rival, as Védrines was losing valuable time with his slapstick navigation. He landed on the wrong field at Bristol and had to hire a car to find the actual control setup, which fortunately was only a few fields away. He had to use flares to take off and land again, but after a short cross-country flight, he glided down only a few yards from where Conneau's Blériot was being serviced.

Groping about over Newcastle, Cody narrowly missed some cottage chimneys, and finally put down at Langley Moor where he smashed his undercarriage, and, of course, his propeller. He sent a telegram to Laffan's Plain for a new airscrew, and set to work to repair the landing gear himself.

The finish of the race came on Wednesday, July 26. Both Védrines and Conneau took off from Bristol at 4:50 A.M., and were soon churning over the Mendip Hills in Somersetshire in fairly good weather. By now Védrines was getting the most out of his Morane, and gradually gained on Conneau, but it was a hopeless task, as he had only 280 miles in which to make up an hour's flying time. When he reached Exeter he had picked up three minutes, and at Salisbury he had cut Conneau's lead by eleven minutes.

Then the Navy lieutenant began to retaliate, and by the time they reached Brighton, Conneau had regained 1½ minutes.

The rest was easy. After a short rest at the famous seaside resort, they drank a glass of champagne apiece, and set out for Brooklands. Again, Conneau landed first in his weary Blériot, his lead well protected. He had completed the Circuit-of-Britain course in 22 hours, 28 minutes flying time. Védrines was 70 minutes behind in the total count. Conneau was given a wild, enthusiastic welcome, but once the formalities were over, Lord Northcliffe gave Védrines a solatium of $1000, after which an astonishing display of sentiment swept through the British public. The *Financial Times* opened a subscription list for Védrines with a sum of $500. James Elliman, a patent medicine manufacturer, contributed $5000, and Grahame-White organized a special flying display at his Hendon field where Védrines appeared and put on an amusing flying show while wearing full evening dress. It seems that he and Conneau were due to appear at a *Daily Mail* banquet at the Savoy Hotel, and Jules was afraid there would not be enough time to change his clothes.

While all this was taking place, Valentine and Cody plodded on. Hamel had become ill at Edinburgh, and had been advised to quit. A week after the start, Valentine in his battered *Antoinette* streaked into Brooklands, and Cody arrived the next day in the only all-British machine to complete the circuit. While Conneau and Védrines were being lauded at one of London's finest hotels, Cody and Valentine toasted each other over a modest supper at the Blue Bird cafe in Brooklands. As Harry Harper wrote in the *Daily Mail*, the outstanding feature of the great race was not Conneau's narrow victory, but rather the spread of time that separated the two Frenchmen from their nearest British competitors.

The Royal Flying Corps Is Formed

From the British point of view, however, some good did come from the Circuit-of-Britain, for the next year the War Office grudgingly granted £320,000 (then $1,600,000) to the development of a military arm. Thirty-six aircraft were purchased, only half of which were British-built, and an organization known as the Royal Flying Corps that had broken away from the ties of the Royal Engineers was formed, and was expected at first to assume both Army and Navy duties. The Central Flying School was established at Upavon where provisions were made to train ninety-one military, forty naval, and fifteen civilian pilots. Only twenty-five aircraft were provided for this bold effort.

It was soon seen that this broad program could not be carried out, so a Military Wing was formed at Farnborough, and a Naval Wing at Eastchurch. All this set up a series of military trials in which British manufacturers were invited to compete in order to develop aeroplanes suitable for these proposed training operations. Later on, owing to the shortage of British entries, the military trials had to be opened to all comers, as proposals were being considered for the formation of seven squadrons of twelve planes each. The balloons and airships were handed over to the Naval Wing.

These military trials proved to be a rewarding idea for in the 1912 program the British received another shock when only one British-built aircraft passed the simple tests. This was Colonel Cody's redesigned *Cathedral* biplane. The machine was big, ungainly, and ill-suited for military work, though it had taken first-prize money. British military men therefore had to revise their views, and reconsider machines already built by Avro, Bristol, Farman, and Sopwith, and with the aid and co-operation of these manufacturers, the Royal Aircraft Factory was set up to produce only military aircraft.

Further details on the development of the world's air arms will be presented in the next chapter.

Hap Arnold's Aerial Hoax

During the summer of 1911 a young aviator from Boston, Harry Atwood, decided to make a name for himself by flying a Burgess-Wright biplane from his home town to the nation's capital at Washington, D.C. The proposed flight was hailed in the Boston newspapers as "the greatest cross-country flight in the history of American aviation."

An interesting feature was that Atwood was one of the few civilian pilots with a license, for by 1911 most airmen were members of the Army or Navy, young officers who had been induced to take to the air. There were comparatively few nonservice pilots.

Atwood was twenty-seven years old when he decided to make this flight, and from all accounts an interesting personality. The machine he depended on was a Wright model that had been built by a new concern, known only as the Burgess Company of Marblehead, Massachusetts. This organization had started out as a subsidiary company of the Curtiss Aeroplane and Motors Corporation, and specialized in the construction of seaplanes to Curtiss designs. Later they built Wright types under license, and then adopted the patents of J. W. Dunne, a well-known British designer, and turned out what was called the Burgess-Dunne machine.

Atwood took off from Boston on June 30, and landed at New London, Connecticut, on his first leg. His next flight took him all the way to New York City where he thrilled the metropolitan area by flying around the 642-foot tower of the Singer Building before coming to a halt on Governors Island. After these two successful hops, the eastern newspapers kept the public in a high key of excitement. In no time Washington was agog, and an official of the Washington Chamber of Commerce hurried to New York to make certain that Atwood would continue on and land in Washington, and not fall for the blandishments of the New York crowds and remain there. The young Bostonian assured him that it would be Washington, or bust!

The date of this meeting between Atwood and the man from Washington was July 1, 1911, and at this particular time a young Army lieutenant who was stationed seven miles from Washington at College Park, Maryland, had just set a new local mark by flying at an altitude of 2500 feet above the capital. But in the planning for Atwood's arrival, his feat was ignored. Meanwhile in New York Atwood was experiencing propeller trouble, and it turned out that he had flown over the state of Connecticut without proper credentials. He had to spend some valuable time in soothing the officials of the Nutmeg State before he could take to the air again, and as a result was grounded until July 4.

His take-off from Governors Island was perfect, and Washington was all set for his appearance, but as the hours went by, afternoon turned into night, but still no news of Atwood. Finally word was received that the Boston flier had run into heavy winds and had had to make a landing at Atlantic City. These conditions continued for day after day, although the Washington crowds were assured time after time that Mr. Atwood had taken off again and was on his way.

It was true that Atwood had started up as promised, but a young bulldog that had been brought to the field to watch the historic operation, decided that the propellers were threatening him, and took a lunge at one. That ended the bulldog—and the propeller. It was July 10 before Atwood climbed into the air again and headed south. By this time the Washington population was completely wrung out in anticipation, but great crowds occupied the open spaces and prominent corners once more, and continued the long vigil.

Inside the Capitol building Congress was in session and Vice-President James S. Sherman was presiding over the Senate. Every so often someone would cry, "Here he comes! Atwood is here!" and the Senators and Representatives would stream out on the lawns to stare up, searching for the elusive Bostonian. Finally, after many false alarms, a tiny speck was seen off to the north, and it grew and grew until it unquestionably was an aeroplane.

"Atwood's here!" everyone screamed, and that ended all work in Washington for that day. The little machine approached, and then, just as Atwood had done in New York, the pilot began circling high buildings, darting down low and roaring along the wide streets of the city. Everyone went wild, regardless of the fact that many air regulations were being broken. It didn't matter. Atwood was here.

But the wild-flying biplane did not land; instead it turned around and disappeared in the direction from which it had come. The people who had wished to shake the Bostonian's hand were keenly disappointed, and the Chamber-of Commerce had to hold off the formal reception they had planned, as Atwood did not appear that day.

The next morning the newspapers were headlined with details of a great aerial hoax. It was not Harry Atwood who had thrilled everyone the day before, but a young Army flier from College Park. Knowing that all Washington was set for an aerial display, Henry Harley Arnold decided to give them one with a government machine. He saw no harm in it, but 50,000 people were completely deceived, including the Vice-President of the United States, members of Congress, and many big names in government circles.

Atwood did not show up for several days, July 14 to be exact. After taking off from Atlantic City he had had to land at Baltimore. The next day he tried again but did not get to Washington; he came down at College Park instead. That evening he made another valiant try but cracked up on take-off, so it was not until July 14 that he finally completed the 461 mile journey, after 17 hours, 12 minutes of actual flying time.

But by this time enthusiasm was aroused again. President Taft was on hand to greet Atwood, and the formal reception was finally held. The success of this venture encouraged Atwood to try another long-distance flight on August 14, 1911, when he completed a trip from St. Louis to New York, a distance of 1266 miles in 28 hours, 35 minutes, with eleven stops. He arrived at his goal on August 25.

Very few aviation enthusiasts remember Harry Atwood, but the young Army lieutenant who "substituted" for him on the Washington flight, became a five-star general, better known as "Hap" Arnold, who headed the United States Army Air Force in World War II.

No sooner had Atwood's triumphs been penned into the records than Calbraith P. Rodgers, a New Yorker, broke all records with a first transcontinental flight between New York and Long Beach, California. He covered 4231 miles with thirty stops en route in an elapsed time of 49 days. His actual time in the air was 3 days, 10 hours, 4 minutes. This flight was another cliff-hanger account, as the newspapers followed Rodgers' flight day by day, crack-up by crack-up, until at last the airman floundered into Long Beach on December 10.

The Golden Years

The Circuit-of-Britain was perhaps the last of the great air races for it marked a fitting finale to the period of trial-and-error experimentation, and gallant individual endeavor. Within a short time a flight by Védrines from France to Egypt created hardly a ripple of interest. Women were taking up the sport, both in the United States and Europe. The first of her sex to gain a pilot's certificate was Mlle. Helene Dutrieu of Paris. On December 15, 1909, she made a one-hour flight covering more than 60 kilometers, and won the 2000-franc *Coupe Femina* prize. Four months later—April 20, 1910—she carried a passenger, and in September 1910 set a new world's altitude record for women by carrying a passenger to 1300 feet. In America the first women's pilot's license was issued to Harriet Quimby of Boston in July 1911, and she was the first of her sex to fly the English Channel. Mathilde Moisant was taught to fly by her brother John. Miss Moisant held the American altitude record for women with a mark of 1500 feet, but she gave up flying in 1912 following an accident. Katherine Stinson of Detroit and Ruth Law of Chicago, both became well-known stunt and exhibition pilots.

Mlle. Dutrieu, who died in 1961, had been a trick bicycle rider, and the sensation of Europe in her daring and ability to turn somersaults in the air while her cycle was in motion. Her first solo flight was made aboard a Santos-Dumont *Demoiselle* monoplane—a single-seater—and from that time on she was setting altitude and endurance records that left the aviation world breathless. In 1913 she was awarded the Legion of Honor, and it has been stated that during World War I she was the only woman pilot to fly as a member of the Paris Air Guard that defended the city against German Zeppelins and bombers.

In September 1910 she thrilled the world by flying nonstop from Ostend to Bruges, and later that same day frightened thousands of spectators in the streets of Ostend by circling a historic belfry spire, and then zooming to an altitude of 1300 feet. All this after many male airmen had tried to dissuade Mlle. Dutrieu from attempting the twenty-eight-mile flight, warning her that she would not be able to withstand the rigors and strain of the journey.

A few months later at Etampes, France, she completed a 158-mile nonstop flight in 2 hours, 58 minutes. She made a visit to the United States in 1911 and charmed everyone with her beauty, figure—and jewelry. She often flew in competition with men, and in the King's Cup, flown at Florence, Italy, she was the only woman in a field of fourteen, but she defeated every man entered against her. She was eighty-four years old when she died.

Airmail, now an accepted part of international communications, was first flown in the United States on September 14, 1911, by Earle Ovington who carried a pouch of mail made up at a temporary post office, established at Sheepshead Bay, Long Island. It was flown from there to the post office at Jamaica, and the United States Post Office Department issued a special stamp for the occasion.

America's longest over-water flight, yet attempted, was made by Lieutenants J. H. Towers and T. G. Ellyson of the United States Navy when, on October 25, 1911, they flew from Annapolis, Maryland, to within two miles of Fort Monroe, Virginia, in 2 hours, 27 minutes. The flight was made in a Curtiss seaplane at an average altitude of 1000 feet.

Frank Coffyn, a New Yorker and one of the first men accepted by the Wrights in their group of American pupils, contributed much to the art of seaplane flying. In 1912 he fitted pontoons to a Wright biplane and took off amid floating ice on the Hudson River, flew upstream to Grant's Tomb, then back to circle the Statue of Liberty, and finally returned to the Battery. He also successfully flew under the Manhattan and Brooklyn bridges. On another occasion he flew down New York Bay to catch a transatlantic liner and put aboard a belated passenger.

The year 1912 also saw Germany take top honors in the world's first seaplane meet held at Monaco, March 24–31 when a pilot named Fischer, flying a Farman biplane fitted with pontoons, won the event on points, beating French, British, and American contestants. Hugh Robinson, aboard a Curtiss seaplane, finished fourth. In an exhibition connected with the event, Fischer carried four passengers, two of whom stood on the pontoons during the flight.

Another passenger-carrying flight of some interest was made on October 6, 1912, at the Johannistal flying field near Hamburg, Germany. The passenger was a Von Arnim, and the pilot Anthony H. G. Fokker, a Dutch aviation engineer who was to design many of Germany's World War I warplanes.

New marks were set, and records toppled everywhere until the public was unable to keep up with the pace of aviation. Men went for height, distance, endurance, and practiced to perfect new maneuvers in the air. On September 23, 1913, Roland Garros dared the first long over-water flight, successfully crossing the Mediterranean Sea when he flew from Frejuz aerodrome near Cannes to Bizerte, Tunisia, a distance of 558 miles in 8 hours, 55 minutes. M. G. Legagneaux, another French airman, broke all existing altitude records when, on December 28, 1913, he climbed to 20,090 feet, a mark that stood for some time.

The colorful Adolphe Pégoud is said to have been the first man to loop-the-loop in an aeroplane, a display that became a standard feature at all air shows prior to the war. But the last meaningful effort of this prewar era was halted before it could be put into operation by the conflagration that was to engulf the world between 1914–18. This was the proposal by Lieutenant John Cyril Porte of the British Navy to make an aeroplane flight across the Atlantic Ocean. Porte had designed a seaplane that he believed was capable of making the trip, and his effort was backed by Rodman Wanamaker of New York. The flying boat, named *America,* was built by Glenn Curtiss at Hammondsport, and was powered by two 90-horsepower Curtiss engines. After a number of successful test flights over Lake Keuka during July 1914 all final preparations to make the attempt were well under way when the war broke out. Lieutenant Porte was recalled to England and almost immediately was put in charge of the Royal Naval Air Station at Felixstowe, and commissioned to build a number of flying boats along the lines of the Curtiss-built *America,* but incorporating many improvements. But it was 1917 before this particular type was ready for patrols. In the meantime Lieutenant Porte devoted considerable time to smaller types known as *Baby* seaplanes, and the work went along until he produced the famous "F" type of flying boats that were to carry out the valuable Spider Web patrols off the North Hinder Light Vessel.

Other versions of the original *America* built at the Curtiss factory became the famed "NC" boats of the United States Navy, one of which, the NC-4, was the first aeroplane to cross the Atlantic in 1919.

Porte's valiant effort was the last of the Golden Years. The Great War was to take all that these gallant men had produced and mold it into a new arm of military service.

Military Aviation

Modern-day readers of aviation action in World War I are amused or confounded to learn that little fighting in the air was recorded during the opening weeks of the conflict. When aviation historians present day-by-day accounts of those early weeks and state that only reconnaissance missions were carried out, some readers assume that this was an early twentieth-century version of the "phony" war that marked the opening months of World War II.

Why didn't airmen of that day blast their opposite numbers out of the sky? Why weren't machine guns mounted the minute war was declared? There had been a lot of prewar talk about war-in-the-air, and a few popular novelists had written engrossing stories of prophetic aerial battles, but when a first-class war was provided, neither side seemed to make any effort toward offensive action. The airmen just fluttered about, checking on the ground movements of enemy troops, drawing maps of behind-the-lines areas, or trying to aim pocket cameras at the landscape below. No one took offensive measures of any kind.

It must be stated, however, that some effort had been made to develop a warplane, and in a few instances aeronautical designers had foreseen the future and had tried to meet any possible situation.

For instance, in 1913 Grahame-White produced what was listed as the Type 6 Military Biplane, which was exhibited at the Olympia Show that year. This was a pusher plane, powered with an Austro-Daimler engine, and had a Colt machine gun mounted in the front cockpit of the nacelle. Photographs of this machine are still available, but there is no record of its ever being flown as a military aircraft, or that the gun was ever fired in the air. Grahame-White turned out another version of this plane early in 1914. It was called the Type 11 Warplane, but its only claim to military fame was that it was intended only as a reconnaissance machine. It was not armed in any manner. It never went into production.

T. O. M. Sopwith also dabbled in the military field, concentrating at first on a few flying boats intended for naval operations. In 1913 he produced a torpedo seaplane for that specific task, but we do not know whether the Royal Navy ever made actual torpedo tests with the machine. His famous *Tabloid* biplane that won the 1914 Schneider Cup contest at Monaco was, of course, the basic machine from which the long line of Sopwith fighters (Pup, One-and-one-half Strutter, Camel, Snipe, Salamander, and Dolphin) were hatched. He also produced what was called the Sopwith Gunbus (not to be confused with the Vickers

Gunbus), but again there is no authentic record of its ever being flown or carrying any form of aerial armament. Some data sheets state that a Lewis gun was mounted in the nose of the nacelle, but none is to be noted in what good photographs are available. The detailed drawings extant do not show any gun mounting.

To compete in the military trials competitions of those days, the Vickers company probably came the closest to developing a real warplane before hostilities broke out. This was natural as the company had taken over the Hiram Maxim machine-gun interests, and after an unsatisfactory experiment in the lighter-than-air field, Vickers bought the manufacturing rights to the French R.E.P. monoplane designed by Robert Esnault Pelterie. Eight versions of this machine were built and flown successfully between 1911–13. By 1913 the company felt the urge to develop its own line, and first showed a two-seater pusher powered by a nine-cylindered Monosoupape Gnome engine. This was known as the E.F.B.1 (Experimental Fighting Biplane), and was equipped with a machine gun mounted in the nose of the duralumin-covered nacelle, and moved in a slot that allowed 60-degree vertical and horizontal sweeps. From this model was developed a line of E.F.B. machines, all mounting a front gun, either on trunnion mountings or on a pillar. A variant of this type eventually became what was known as the Vickers Gunbus, Britain's first two-seater fighter, but it did not go into production until late 1914, and was not available for front-line service until early 1915.

It will be seen, therefore, that offensive war—fighting in the air—was impossible with the equipment at hand. It must be recalled that the aeroplane of early 1914 was only eleven years older than the machine first flown by the Wrights at

Kitty Hawk. During those few years a handful of men had worked to raise its performance from 31 miles an hour to about 58 miles an hour. Its weight-carrying ability, generally speaking, had been improved so that one or two passengers could be carried. Under ideal weather conditions flights of a hundred miles or more at heights of 2000 or 3000 feet were possible. In fact, one historian of that time proudly recounted that under normal conditions the movement of the machine while flying was "smooth enough to enable the passenger to use both hands for writing notes, sketching or taking photographs," and that with practice he could use moderately powerful field glasses.

It was agreed generally that the aeroplane of 1913–14 could remain in the air while being turned in a short circle and thus kept above any particular spot for a considerable time. But in the same breath it was admitted that natural phenomena, such as "vertical currents and whirls" might unexpectedly wreck a machine; that the breakage of a single stay could cause immediate disaster; and that any defect of the engine or fuel supply would "enforce a descent to earth." These were general factors to be reviewed in peacetime. In war, however, there were other conditions to be reckoned with, and before responsible officials could form an accurate opinion as to the utility of aeroplanes for active service in war, it was necessary to determine the effect of artillery or infantry fire and the probability of hits against the value of observation from a flying machine. Could men aboard an aeroplane fire light weapons at terrestrial objects? (No one considered the exchange of light weapons in the air.) Could ground targets be hit by bombs "thrown or discharged from flying machines?" Could aeronauts record and communicate the information they might gather while flying above the enemy's territory?

It is apparent that from the beginning, burdened with the application of the aeroplane to military tactics, men had to consider what they had to work with and to analyze carefully the limited capacity of the aeroplane—and the man or men operating it. It must be remembered that never before had such a device been employed in warfare. It is pointless to argue that on November 1, 1911, a Lieutenant Gavotti of Italy dropped six small bombs on the enemy lines during the Italian-Turkish war, as this illegal act in no way influenced the outcome. At best, this bombing was nothing more than an irresponsible escapade.

The most reasonable use to which the 1914 aeroplane could be put in warfare was reconnaissance; the examination by trained officers of definite tracts of territory or localities with a view of ascertaining the nature of the country, the roads, the railroads, the rivers, the bridges, the battle positions, the nature and extent of fortifications, positions, numbers and nature of enemy troops, movement of supply trains, positions of magazines, military depots, and any military deployment that was in progress.

Any bombardment might possibly delay or harass the enemy, but the discharge of light bombs on encampments, bivouacs, or even on large bodies of troops had not been attempted. Some authorities agreed that incendiary bombs might be dropped on enemy supply dumps with some effect, but, unfortunately, the munitions makers had not attempted to devise an incendiary bomb. Direct attacks on convoys or marching troops might be made by flying machines that carried machine guns, but as stated before, no such equipment was available at the outbreak of war. Both sides had small fleets of aircraft, but neither had any sound idea as to how they might be employed.

What It Took

Only in the field of reconnaissance could any accurate conclusions be drawn, as on one or two occasions airmen had carried out such missions during peacetime maneuvers. But any talk of bombs, explosive or incendiary, was mere conjecture because no efficient missiles were available, and no aircraft had been fitted with suitable racks. Also no one had attempted to work out a set of tables by which such missiles could be dropped with any degree of accuracy. There was no such instrument as a bombsight.

Of course, if any of the above missions could be carried out, it stood to reason that the other side would plan counterattacks, but no one considered the possibility of opposition from enemy flying machines, and it is useless to question why such a countermeasure had not been conceived. The men responsible for the development of air power were not blessed with 20/20 hindsight. The possibility had to come through experience.

But they did appreciate the contingency of antiaircraft fire, although only Krupps had done much toward developing a high-angle artillery weapon capable of scoring hits on moving aircraft flying at 60 miles per hour, some 3000 feet above the ground. They knew that direct hits by impact shells were out of the question, but there might be some hope in the use of the shrapnel shell. At that time this consisted of a metal case containing a small charge of explosive sufficient to burst the shell, and a fuse that could be set to explode the charge at any required distance from the gun muzzle. The bullets in the metal case, once it was exploded, would spread out over a considerable area at sufficient speed to break or seriously damage any portion of an aeroplane with which they might come in contact.

But to get the most out of such a shell, the ground forces would need a gun that could be elevated to such an angle that the shell would reach the level of the aircraft. The range would have to be accurately known. The fuse would have to be set to burst the shell at the exact moment. Firing tables would have to be devised to aid the gun-layer to aim his weapon, not at the machine itself, but at some computed point ahead of it. This computed point could be known only by determining the distance from the machine at the moment of firing, which in turn was dependent on the known speed of the aircraft, the speed of the projectile, and the distance from the gun.

All this was brand new in the realm of military science. Even when the theory had been conceived, it took a great quantity of ammunition to employ and work out these tables in actual practice. The howitzers of that day could fire shells a little more than 3000 feet, and that particular weapon could traverse through only a comparatively small angle—without having to raise and shift its trail. In early 1914 there was a question as to whether the expenditure of ammunition was justified simply to bring down a reconnaissance machine.

In some European countries special guns that were capable of being elevated almost vertically had been mounted on automobiles and were thus highly mobile, but here again it was considered doubtful policy to expend money, men, and transport on a special arm to be used only for the purpose of combating enemy aircraft. The possibility of concerted infantry fire was also discounted. It was pointed out that although a hundred men conceivably might fire 3000 rounds at a machine crossing over their heads, and they might score a number of hits, many of the shots would have to be fired from uncomfortable or awkward positions, and there would be little time to alter their sights. The range would be unknown, and changing rapidly. Another problem was to know whether the aeroplane in question was friend or foe, as the international insignia had not been considered in the early days of the war, and there were instances where airmen were able to spend many minutes scouting enemy activity with no opposition because the troops below did not know whether the aircraft above was hostile or friendly.

The Gunnery Problem

The reader may still persist in arguing that there was no reason why these early planes could not have been armed with machine guns, but easier said than done, considering the aircraft and their rated performance. Few machines at the outbreak of the war were capable of carrying a two-man crew, fuel for a distant patrol, *and* a machine gun with its mounting and ammunition. Let us take any of the aircraft available to Great Britain, which were fairly representative of the period. Her four organized squadrons went to France equipped with Henri Farmans, Avros, Blériots, and B.E.8s (affectionately known as Bloaters). The Avro of that date was powered with an 80-horsepower Gnome, and was scarcely capable of 80 miles per hour. The Henri Farman (Shorthorn), powered with a 75-horsepower Renault, was rated at only 58 miles per hour. The Blériots were only a few horsepower, and slabs of three-ply, removed from the model that had carried Louis Blériot across the Channel in 1909. The B.E.8 was a dreadful contraption that might cruise along at 65 miles per hour, but it had the misfortune to be powered with a Royal Aircraft Factory engine, of which it was charged that the cylinders blew off in the order of firing. The era of the Camel, Fokker, Triplane, S.E.5, and the Spad was still three years off, and the writer, who first became acquainted with the Royal Flying Corps in 1916, had never heard of any of these historic mounts.

Obviously, the aircraft of 1914 were capable of taking only two men into the air to carry out reconnaissance flights. Despite their billboard-sized wings they could not attain an altitude above 3000 feet, and to burden them further with a machine gun that weighed around 57 pounds and its mounting which added another 50 pounds was out of the question. In addition a spare-parts case, weighing about 15 pounds would have had to be carried, and the ammunition in its belt would have weighed at least 30 pounds. This, of course, was the service weapon of that time, not the stripped-down version available once a synchronization gear had been devised. So in order to mount a machine gun, the plane would have to carry an additional 152 pounds, or the weight of a second passenger.

Later on, the bronze water jackets used on the Vickers types, and the heavy air-cooling fins and jackets necessary on the ground-type Lewis, were dispensed with, cutting down their weight considerably. Lighter and more suitable mountings were devised, but these features were not contrived overnight. They could be produced only when the platform had been improved, or the necessity for such armament became apparent. The progress of aerial armament from the early days of 1914 until the appearance of the Sopwith Salamander 6-gun fighter of 1918 would require a full volume to record.

The Eyes of the Army

The devotion to reconnaissance was based on more than official determination to use the aeroplane only for such work. In both Army and Navy circles the entrenched staff had no use for any such mechanical contrivance; to the military man it was a noisy contraption, and a smelly device; to the Navy man it was immediately placed in the category of the submarine. It was dirty, unkempt, and attracted only the lowest, ragtime types of the service. Whenever the possibility of using the machine for bombing was brought up, artillery men argued that howitzers and Long Toms could do a better job with less hazard, while the blue-water Navy men feared that any success along this line would put a halt to the building of their favored dreadnoughts. Thus, whenever a move was made to improve or increase the military air arm, the stodgy thinkers of both services soon hooted it down because not one of them could foresee that the sky was to become another battlefield no less important than the arenas on land and sea. (I trust I will be forgiven if I point out that today in the mid-1960s the manned-bomber devotees are taking the same attitude toward the new science of guided missiles.)

However, reconnaissance was an important factor in military tactics, and because of its comparative speed, freedom of action, and cheap cost (at that time), the aeroplane was an ideal vehicle for such assignments. Then the idea of its being used as a range-finder for the artillery gradually took shape, and next its immediate advantages over surface means led it to be used to attack the enemy on and behind his own lines, although no great importance was attached to this possibility because in 1913–14 the machine was incapable of transporting a heavy load of offensive matériel. But in a few months all these hopes, or fears, were confirmed, and aircraft designers had to face up to counterattack measures, and devise the fighter plane. But aerial warfare could not be staged until all factors of aerial power were increased. Aircraft had to be bigger, more powerful, and designed to carry the required armament. To put larger and heavier planes into the air, aircraft engines had to be improved to produce the necessary power, and once this weight consideration was accepted, larger aircraft had to be designed to get the engines and their fuel tanks aloft. Thus the inevitable tail chasing went on for more than four years.

Military reconnaissance had been appreciated soon after men learned to fly with powered machines, for when it became obvious that the aeroplane eventually would displace the balloon, tethered or free, a few shrewd men realized that with such a mobile platform, reconnaissance from the air would be of greater value than that obtained by earth-bound cavalry patrols. In fact, as early as 1912 European and British armies were experimenting with aeroplane reconnaissance, and in 1910 the French had already formed an independent air arm, and were training officers in the art of aerial reconnaissance. Their 1911 military maneuvers were planned on a large scale, and pilots and observers outdid themselves carrying out many important patrols, some in most inclement weather. The speed with which they produced good photographs, maps, and reports of "enemy" movement, impressed the French military staff, and as a result three complete aviation groups were immediately established.

Up to this time no specific requirement had been laid

down for military aircraft; any plane with a respectable performance, structural strength, and general adaptability was suitable for reconnaissance missions. But it was soon apparent—to the French at least—that the machine would have to possess offensive power, for so far they had nothing with which to attack troops on the ground or other aircraft in the air.

A new Military Aircraft Competition was organized in which the machines competing would have to fulfill the following requirements: they would have to be two-seaters capable of flying 186 miles, carrying a payload of 660 pounds besides the crew, and be able to maintain a speed of at least 37 miles per hour.

What the payload was to consist of was never discussed or indicated, but on examination of their early war machines it is obvious that aerial bombing was the chief consideration. Machine guns were seldom, if ever, mentioned.

This, and other competitions eventually weeded out the second-raters, and by August 1914 the French Air Service, composed of twenty-one escadrilles of six two-seaters each, and four escadrilles of three single-seaters (reserved for the use of the cavalry), was ready for action. The aircraft selected were the Blériot, Henri Farman, Maurice Farman, Deperdussin, Bréguet, Voisin, Caudron, R.E.P., Nieuport, and a few Blériot single-seaters.

Germany's Air Strength

The Imperial German Air Force was organized on paper as early as 1912, for the Kaiser's military officials had been among the first to appreciate what the Wright brothers had created, and clearly saw the aeroplane as a potential war machine. When the European situation began to seethe, a sum approximating $20,000,000 was offered as prize money to encourage and finance the building of heavier-than-air aircraft and suitable engines. But, strangely enough, little came of this; the top military staff was more interested in Count Zeppelin's miracle gasbags that were establishing passenger-carrying records over all Europe. Everyone was willing to invest in dirigibles, but few civilians could see any financial future in the limited range of the aeroplane.

So obsessed were they with the lighter-than-air concept that one designer produced a winged balloon that was intended to be loaded with bombs, carry a clockwork quick-release gear that would be set according to wind and drift, and at a specified time—presumably when the balloon was over its objective—the release gear would operate. Down would go the balloon, bombs and all. This idea was in fact tried out in October 1914, but the test was a failure when the balloon refused to leave the ground. About thirty years later the Germans released their covey of buzz bombs on Britain, fulfilling their idea of a pilotless air weapon.

Fortunately for Britain, the German Airship Service experienced a discouraging period of development. At one time it seemed on the point of being disbanded after the loss in 1913 of nearly all of its experienced officers in two Zeppelin disasters. Only the delivery of L.3 from Count Zeppelin's factory at Friedrichshafen in May 1914 kept the lighter-than-air service in existence.

It was not until 1911 that an Austrian inventor, Igo Etrich, produced a satisfactory military aeroplane—a model he tried to sell to his own government, but he was turned down. A German Secret Service agent got in touch with Etrich, and the contact resulted in his Taube-design monoplane being purchased outright by officials of the Rumpler factory at Berlin-Kichtenberg. The government ordered Rumplers to turn out twenty Taubes at once, and then sent Herr Etrich back to Austria where he was seldom heard of from then on.

Etrich's Taubes, or "dove" machines, were most efficient for early military work, and in a short time nearly twenty small factories were producing various Etrich types, powered by either Argus or Mercedes engines. The Rumpler model surpassed all others, and on July 9, 1913, Herr Linnekogel, who was chief pilot for the Rumpler factory, set a new altitude record of nearly 20,000 feet—an effort that was to have an important part in Rumpler's future. From that point on the company designers concentrated on height and a rapid rate of climb rather than forward speed. This made their photography and reconnaissance machines the most successful in the German aircraft field.

By the spring of 1913 the German High Command placed orders for additional aircraft, half of which were to be biplanes, the rest monoplanes. The latter were practically all Taube types, and the biplanes were manufactured by Rumpler, Euhler, A.E.G., L.V.G., Ago, and D.W.F. Twelve months later when Germany was making active preparation for war, an Army bill was passed, granting $2,000,000 and what was left of the original design prize of $20,000,000 to the Imperial Air Service. More aircraft were ordered, and the old types replaced. An additional clause in all contracts now specified that all new machines were to be of German manufacture, and were to have seats for a pilot and passenger. In addition, they were to be provided with bomb racks and fittings for an aerial camera. No engines of less than 100 horsepower would be accepted, and a minimum top speed of 65 miles per hour, a ceiling of 8000 feet, and a flight duration of at least four hours were mandatory.

When the August drums rolled, Germany's Air Force was well ahead of that of any other belligerent power. She had thirty-eight Zeppelins, or Schütte-Lanz dirigibles, and more than eighty pilots to handle these giants. In heavier-than-air hangars she had the production of more than three years, totaling 1954 aircraft built to military specifications. Allowing a certain percentage loss for crashes, wear and tear, and unserviceableness, she must have had a thousand aircraft available at the outbreak of war. Thirty-six of these were first-class seaplanes for use over coastal waters.

About a thousand pilots had finished their training, and there were 487 skilled observers, and additional personnel of 2600 to maintain these aircraft. In 1912 there were only twenty-eight airfields in Germany, but at the start of the war this number had been more than doubled.

The Photography Problem

The mention of fittings for an aerial camera brings up another interesting point in this development of military aircraft. Actually, there was no such instrument. Although many attempts had been made to take pictures from the air, nothing of value had been accomplished. A few novelty shots had been made of grandstand crowds from planes flying at about 100 feet, but true military photographs, either vertical or oblique, had not been available prior to the war.

Visual observation carried out by trained men was all well and good—up to a point—but it was soon clear that much detail was either forgotten or missed entirely, and shrewd commanders realized that the work could be properly carried out only by the use of special camera equipment. But where could such equipment be found? There was none.

It is to the credit of the commanding officer of Number 3 Squadron, R.F.C., Major Henry R. M. Brooke-Popham, that the aerial camera was conceived. He had seen how his observers had missed many features during the early war games, and he suggested that they try using a camera. At first they bought their own, or borrowed folding pocket cameras from friends. There was no money to buy anything better, or to set up a photography unit, but they persisted, and early in the war produced a remarkable set of pictures of the defenses around the Isle of Wight. During the First Battle of the Aisne (September 1914) they shot another series that, though fuzzy and amateurish, proved of rare value to GHQ. Following this, two lieutenants and a couple of NCO specialists were ordered to design a more suitable air camera. Co-operating with the Thornton-Pickard Manufacturing Company, this quartet produced a new type of box camera in which the lens was held in the recessed front, a fixed distance from the 5×4 inch plate. The observer held the camera by means of straps or brass handles, leaned over the side of the cockpit, and took his photographs. Satisfactory results were obtained even though eleven separate operations were necessary before he could snap the first picture, and ten separate operations for every subsequent exposure.

With this primitive instrument, the R.F.C. made up a commendable map that was used to plan the Battle of Neuve-Chapelle. The complete German trench system was clearly shown, covering an area from 700 to 1500 yards in depth, depicted on a map to a scale of one to 8000. Fifteen hundred copies of this chart were made and distributed to the infantry and artillery, and what success was enjoyed in the initial assault was plainly due to this pre-battle preparation.

The aeroplane had taken on a single eye, becoming the Cyclops of the air. The thunderbolts it was to hurl were also being forged at the hearths of the munitions makers.

Bombs and Bombers

While there had been a great deal of loose talk concerning the possibility of dropping bombs on enemy targets, there was little justification for the claim. In the first place few of the machines available were capable of carrying a load that would justify a venture into enemy territory. Secondly, there were no projectiles suitable for such attacks. In prewar experiments and at aviation meets, "bomb-dropping" events had been made with bags of flour or oranges, but right up to the outbreak of the war there was no concerted attempt to produce an aerial bomb; one that could be carried aboard and released from an aeroplane in flight. The missiles dropped from the Italian plane in 1911 actually were a form of grenade which were carried in a leather bag, and the detonators were in the pilot's pocket. When he arrived over the Turkish encampment, Lieutenant Gavotti had to take each grenade separately, screw in the detonator, while holding the control stick between his knees, and then toss the missile over the side. He had to circle the area several times to get rid of his load. Early in World War I the primitive bombs were carried in the pilot's pockets, or slung bandoleer-like about his person.

The first aerial bombs were crude, handmade affairs, based on a cylindrical, metal container. In some instances long, glass wine bottles were used, which the airmen casually tossed over the side. The incendiary types were simply canisters of gasoline that were presumed to ignite on impact with the ground. Such bombs were used against German hangars and airship sheds. Another variant of the incendiary bomb was a simple can of explosive that was wrapped with sticky, tarred rope. Burning rope was supposed to fly in all directions when the explosive was ignited.

An early form of fragmentation, or antipersonnel, bomb was contrived from a French melinite shell fitted with guide vanes, but this was detonated with an artillery nose cap that had to be set at "zero" in order to explode on impact. All too often these bombs would explode while being loaded into the primitive racks of that day, and had to be discarded.

Because of the slow speed of the aircraft some bombs had to be fitted with parachutes in order to delay their speed in reaching the ground, as on several occasions aircraft and propellers were damaged by flying debris. In many instances single bombs were lashed to the upper *longerons* with common wrapping cord, and when the airman wished to release them over the target he used his pocketknife.

The first true bomber raid was made against an enemy Zeppelin shed near Bruges on September 22, 1914. All available R.F.C. aircraft took part, each machine carrying six 20-pound bombs. In order to deliver this load, the observers were left behind; the pilots flying alone, and presumably releasing their explosive from primitive racks. From this date on, practically all air bombs were made with a streamlined body form, as it was thought that a more accurate trajectory would be assured. Later tests proved this was not so, but because most World War I bombs were carried outside the aircraft, streamlining the general form made them less of a drag. When bombs were carried within the bomb bays of later machines, they all were made in common cylindrical form to simplify manufacture.

With the improvement of aircraft, bomb sights, and the development of the aerial art, bombs eventually were fully standardized, and were produced as 20-pounders, 50-pounders, and 100-pounders. When the Handley-Page bombers were available, 500-pounders were their standard armament, although before the war was over British airmen had carried and dropped a bomb of over 1000 pounds in weight.

By early 1915 little progress had been made in the production of suitable bombs, and when Flight Sub-Lieutenant R. A. J. Warneford came upon a Zeppelin over Belgium on June 7, 1915, he had only a few fire bombs—primitive incendiary missiles—with which to attack it. Luckily, after dropping five of these devices, LZ.37 went up in flames. Later on various forms of incendiary ammunition calibered for the standard machine guns were used, but this took months and years.

There were no bomb sights, such as were known in World War II. When bombs were dropped, the pilot simply flew over his target, waited until the focal point appeared to be sliding under the leading edge of his biplane, and then hopefully "pulled the plug," a simple Bowden cable that released the bombs. As was to be expected, results depended on the luck or skill of the operator. Then a veritable birdcage device was developed in which some theory of trajectory was worked out. This consisted of a simple open frame, three adjustable "perches," and a stopwatch clamped to the assembly, but like the original aerial camera, it required too many separate adjustments before it could be put into operation.

A more efficient sight was developed later on by the Wimperis company, designers of aeronautical instruments.

Surprisingly, the wireless telegraph of those days was almost instantly adapted and put into use. As early as August 27, 1910, J. A. D. McCurdy had sent a message from an aeroplane over Sheepshead Bay to a ground station where it was received by H. M. Horton. Other aircraft-to-ground contacts had been made by a number of lighter-than-air machines at about the same time. Still, to produce a set and its aerial that would fit into the aeroplane of that period was an accomplishment in itself. On September 24, 1914, during the Battle of the Aisne, Lieutenants D. S. Lewis and B. T. James of Number 4 Squadron, R.F.C., carried out an important artillery shoot while flying over an enemy battery. Their log of that afternoon reads as follows:

4:02 P.M.   A very little short. Fire! Fire!
4:04 P.M.   Fire again. Fire again.
4:12 P.M.   A little short; line O.K.
4:15 P.M.   Short. Over, over and a little left.
4:20 P.M.   You were just between two batteries.
            Search two hundred yards each side of your last shot. Range O.K.
4:22 P.M.   You have hit them.
4:26 P.M.   Hit. Hit.
4:37 P.M.   Your last shot in the middle of three batteries in action; search all round within three hundred yards of your last shot and you have them.
4:42 P.M.   I am coming home now.

A short time later Lieutenants Lewis and James were killed in action, but their historic start had set the pattern for a new military science. Within a few weeks aerial observers were spotting shot-by-shot artillery fire, and before the war was moving into its last year, the radio telephone was being used between crews of Bristol Fighter planes.

Guns and Gunnery

We now come to a point in this history that has intrigued aviation enthusiasts for the past half century; a subject that has suffered from more misconceptions and deliberate evasion than any other concerning military aviation. There has been a widespread assumption for years that Anthony Fokker, designer of the Fokker planes for the German Air Service, conceived and produced a fixed machine gun that fired its bullets through the whirling blades of the propeller. With this device—exclusive with them—the German airmen are said to have driven all Allied aircraft out of the sky. The phrase "Fokker Fodder" was based on this false supposition, though nowhere in the records of World War I are there figures to substantiate these repeated statements. Anthony Fokker did not invent the first machine gun that fired through the blades of the propeller. His Fokker E.1 was not the first plane to fire a machine gun directly forward. The Fokker E.1 did not gain mastery of the air for the Germans. It simply was the best single-seater fighter, armed with a synchronized gun, over a very short period of time. Although it was the first machine fitted with a *synchronized* (front-firing) weapon, it was in fact woefully exploited, as were many other outstanding inventions such as the tank, poison gas, flame throwers, and the true concept of the single-seater fighter. Had the E.1 first been produced in great numbers in secrecy, and full squadrons of these machines sent into action against the Allies, there is no question but that the Fokker would have become a real scourge. Instead, it was doled out, one by one, to selected airmen. It was quickly identified, and measures were taken to cope with it.

To begin from the beginning. What air fighting took place at the outbreak of war, was engaged in by aerial gunners, and throughout the length of the war these young men bore more than their share of the fight, although most writers have handed the combat palm to the pilot of the single-seater fighter. To some extent this is understandable, as fighter pilots could enumerate their successes and be credited with individual exploits, whereas aerial gunners fought in flight, or squadron, formations with little thought of personal claim or credit. In fact it was difficult under these conditions to decide just who had downed an enemy aeroplane because in most cases the aerial gunners fought as a team, not as duelists. So it is impossible to state who contributed more to the cause, the fighter pilot or the aerial gunner.

In the beginning aerial gunners were picked haphazardly from the ranks of mechanics, motorcar drivers, or the clerical staff. None had had in-air gunnery training, their chief qualifications being the ability to load and fire a cavalry carbine, to be immune to airsickness, and have jacket pockets that could accommodate half-bricks for dropping on enemy aircraft. For the more definitive work of an observer, commissioned officers were induced to volunteer with the promise of becoming pilots after reasonable periods of front-line flying.

The gunnery detail was at first carried out with carbines or shotguns, and whenever an enemy machine was seen snooping about over the Allied lines, the aerial gunner amused himself by potting away whenever his pilot could bring him within range. The pilot might join in by firing a few rounds from his Webley revolver, but very little came of all this belligerency, although Captain G. W. Mapple-beck of the R.F.C. returned from a reconnaissance patrol in mid-September 1914 with a German pistol bullet in his shoulder.

When it was realized that aeroplanes were actually carrying out important reconnaissance patrols, the GHQ officials decided that something should be done to put a stop to this snooping, and the aerial gunners were ordered to be more determined in their hunting. The Germans retaliated in kind, and Lieutenant V. Waterfell was shot down and killed over Ath, Belgium, the first casualty of the 7589 who were to die in the British flying services during the next four years of air combat.

When it was obvious that the machines would have to be armed, special clips on which to mount Army rifles were fitted to the aircraft. In most cases, the gunners or observers who manned these weapons sat in the front seats of the biplane types, and naturally were handicapped by having to aim and fire through the network of struts, stays, flying wires, the whirling propeller, and fluttering wingtips. Toward the end of September two Bristol Scouts were delivered, one to Number 3 and one to Number 5 Squadrons, both armed with a rifle on each side of the pilot's cockpit, and mounted to shoot at an angle of 45 degrees to avoid hitting the propeller tips. Whether they ever went into action with any success has not been recorded.

Rifles, shotguns, and carbines gave the gunners some small measure of satisfaction, but the German aircraft were so superior in gaining and maintaining height that it was almost impossible for the British or French planes to get at them. German Rumplers would be buzzing over the Allied areas while their observers drew maps, took photographs or wrote out detailed reports completely undisturbed. Frustrated Allied airmen floundered about 2000 feet below vainly shooting off carbines at the inquisitive Jerries.

Since they could not vent their spleen on the enemy airmen above, the Allied fliers took it out on the ground troops below. Various forms of steel darts were dumped over the side, and multipointed versions of these missiles were dropped along roads to cripple enemy cavalry or transport horses. But generally speaking, the rivalry and competition that were to mark the next four years of conflict were gradually being developed by the aerial gunners using standard rifles and carbines.

There were many rumors that someone, somewhere, had taken a machine gun into the air, but there never were any names, places, or reports of actual results. But by early 1915 it was quite evident that the aeroplane would have to be efficiently armed, and that one possibility rested on the idea of mounting a gun, or guns, so it could be fired in the direction in which the aeroplane was flying. The gun, or guns, had, however, to be mounted convenient to the pilot for reloading or the clearance of stoppages. And there was the rub. Any gun mounted so conveniently would have to be somewhere behind the propeller.

The British overcame this, first by selecting a pusher model with the engine and propeller behind the pilot, and the gun could be placed anywhere that was convenient to the airman. They already had variations of the pusher Farman machines, and newer types, such as the F.E.2b and the F.E.8, a single-seater pusher, were coming out of the Royal Aircraft Factory. Along with this, the Aircraft Manufacturing Company was building a De Havilland single-seater pusher known as the D.H.2. All these aeroplanes could mount front-firing guns that did not rely on synchronization gears. In the meantime other British manufacturers and experimenters were working on the interrupter-gear idea. The Sopwith company was developing a device, conceived originally by a Sergeant Kauper, and eventually produced as the Sopwith-Kauper gear. This was first applied to the new Sopwith two-seater, known as the 1½-Strutter, a name that emanated from the splayed center-section struts —the inner short, the outer long. It also carried the first of the famed Scarff ring mounting, giving the aerial gunner a movable weapon. Thus, Britain had a two-seater fighter equipped with both a synchronized front gun *and* a free-moving rear-seat weapon, long before any other air force could put one on the front.

During all this development other British squadrons were carrying on with pushers in which both the pilot and the gunner could fire forward without concern for the propeller. A French mechanic, a Sergeant Alkan, devised an inter-rupter gear for the Lewis gun that also was being tested out by the Royal Flying Corps. Major A. V. Bettington of Number 1 Aircraft Depot developed what was known as the Arsiad gear that was fitted to a number of British machines in 1915. The Scarff-Dibovsky gear, the joint invention of Lieutenant Commander V. V. Dibovsky of the Imperial Russian Navy and Mr. F. W. Scarff of the British Admi-ralty's Air Department, was adopted by the Vickers works, and fitted to a number of British aircraft.

The most important step in the synchronized-gun field was made by George Constantinesco, a Rumanian inventor who turned out a hydraulic gear through which the neces-sary impulses to control the weapon were transmitted through a length of copper tubing and a small reservoir containing a mixture of oil and kerosene under pressure. The Constantinesco gear could be adapted to any aircraft or type of gun. It will be seen that the British were soon in the field with several first-class machines that were equipped with a synchronized machine gun, and, equally important, with a first-class two-seater fighter employing both the fixed front gun and a flexible weapon for the gunner-observer.

It was well they did, for the R.F.C. had to assume the offensive well inside the enemy lines, once the war settled down to its trench stalemate.

Roland Garros Again

When the war started, the French airman Roland Garros was in Germany giving flying exhibitions and talks on the value of the aeroplane in peace and war. One day as he was returning to his hotel he learned that German troops had invaded Belgium and his beloved France. He packed his bag, and leaving by a rear exit he skulked back to the field where he had been making his flying exhibitions. As the whole ground staff was occupied in a nearby *Gasthaus* toasting the Kaiser and Germany's gallant Army, Garros had no trouble in dragging his Morane from its shed, starting its Le Rhône engine, and taking off for the nearby Swiss border. His unannounced departure created a great furor, it being concluded that during his exhibitions the popular Frenchman had photographed every fortress in Germany.

When he reached France, Roland immediately reported for military service, and soon found himself among many old friends, such as Armand Pinsard, Jules Védrines, Eugene Gilbert, and Marc Pourpe, who had introduced a young man from Wallingford, Connecticut, Raoul Lufbery, to the French Aviation. All these men made a great contribution to military aviation, but it was Roland Garros who

first gave the machine gun wings. He carried to its ulti-
mate concept a plan that originated with Eugene Gilbert.

It was Gilbert who first conceived the idea of mounting
a fixed machine gun to fire through the blades of the propeller, but his experiments ended in tragedy, and he for-
sook the scheme. He had wrapped a length of steel tape
around the butt of each blade, after figuring that if he
mounted a gun behind the prop and pulled the trigger, a
small percentage of the bullets would strike the propeller,
but if the blades were protected with some tough metal,
the bullets would ricochet off and do no damage.

In fact, during December 1914, Gilbert took a Morane
monoplane, mounted a Hotchkiss gun above the engine
cowling, put the wrapping of steel tape around the blades
and prepared to try it out. The plane was set up before a
sandbagged wall, the engine started, and the trigger pulled.
But, unfortunately, two young officers who were assisting
in the test, were killed by deflected slugs. Heartbroken by
the tragedy, Gilbert gave up his experiment.

Garros had conceived the same plan but he devised a set
of deflector collars made of armorplate that could be bolted
over the propeller blades. These were well thought out and
efficiently designed, and when test-fired the bullets that
struck the deflector plate continued on ahead at a sharp
angle, doing no damage to the pilot, the machine, or the
assistants who stood nearby. Less than 7 per cent of the
bullets fired actually hit the deflector plate.

All this testing was carried out in February 1915, but
Garros was not ready to try his device against the enemy
until April 1, 1915. On that day he caught an Albatros two-
seater behind Epernay, and shot it down with one short
burst. Ten days later he trapped two Aviatik two-seaters,
and employing the same strategy—moving behind them—he

roared in with his Hotchkiss gun firing, and shot down both of them. The following afternoon he caught an L.V.G., also a two-seater, and shot it down near Dunkirk. Two days later one of Germany's newer Aviatiks was spotted flying toward the French lines. The pilot quickly dumped his load of light bombs, and his gunner punctured Garros's reserve fuel tank. Trailing a long cloud of gasoline vapor, the Frenchman disregarded the possibility of fire in the air and closed in. The German observer died with five bullets in his chest, and the pilot took several in his head, some of which went on through and ignited the fuel line. The Aviatik went down in flames and burned to a cinder in a marsh.

The World's First Ace

Garros had scored five victories in sixteen days, and the night of the sixteenth day he was cited for the Legion of Honor. He was the toast of Paris, and the gay boulevardiers hailed their newest hero. "Oh, that Garros! That Roland Garros! Five enemy machines he has destroyed! That Garros is an ace!"

The term "ace" was a popular catchword of the day in France. Any newsworthy person who had performed anything unusual was an ace. The latest winning cyclist was an "ace." The newest popular jockey was an "ace." It was natural for the word to be applied to Roland Garros.

This reference was overheard by an American newspaperman who interpreted it to mean any pilot who downed five enemy planes. In his next dispatch to New York he applied the word to the name of Roland Garros, and it became the journalistic standard by which a fighter pilot in any air service was rated.

So Roland Garros became the world's first ace, as well as the man who revolutionized aerial warfare. He was invited to appear before the Directorate of Military Aeronautics to present his views on this new art of aerial combat. The date was set for April 25, but Roland Garros could not keep the appointment. On the afternoon of April 19, 1915, Garros took off to bomb the railroad sidings at Courtrai. He flew all the way to his target without seeing an enemy plane, so he cut his Le Rhône engine, went into an attack glide, swept over the freight yards, and dropped his bombs. When he tried to switch on his engine again, nothing happened. The propeller just windmilled in the slipstream. He knew immediately what was wrong and probably swore at his imbecility. In the long glide for the Courtrai freight yard the spark plugs had oiled up, as he had forgotten to "burn" them off with intermittent blipping of the ignition switch. He had no alternative but to stretch his glide until he found a suitable spot to land.

He came down near Ingelmunster about 40 miles from the Dutch border. His first thought was to destroy his plane and the details of the propeller's protective collar, the secret of his front-firing gun. He did his best, but the wing fabric and the spruce framework were damp and refused to burn. The best he could do was to create a telltale smoke smudge.

A party of German soldiers shortly arrived, and Garros was taken prisoner. As soon as the machine was examined by a group of Air Service technicians, the bullet-streaked deflection plates were noticed, and the secret of Garros's front-firing gun revealed. The Germans moved fast. The French *cocardes* were daubed out, and the Morane Bullet flown to Berlin where it was handed to Anthony Fokker who was building his Fokker E.1s for the German Air Force.

What Fokker Learned

Fokker was ordered to reproduce the same idea and fit it to a number of his light monoplanes, but the young Dutch engineer did not like the arrangement, and conceived instead the idea of pressing the trigger only when there was no blade in front of the gun barrel. With that dreamy plan, he gradually worked out a basic design for an interrupter gear. The gun had to be interrupted in its rate of fire whenever there was a propeller blade in line with the gun barrel.

The rest was easy. Fokker simply fitted a light cam ring to the back of the propeller which depressed a lever that, operating through a series of cranks and rods, either pressed or released the trigger. In theory, the concept worked beautifully; in practice a few bugs had to be worked out to accommodate the irregularity of fire caused by faulty ammunition or friction lags in the German Parabellum gun mechanism. But in five days Fokker had a working model mounted on an E.1 monoplane, and it passed all tests before a group of Air Service officials.

The first service models were given to Oswald Boelcke and Max Immelmann, but they never equaled Roland Garros's score of five planes in sixteen days. It took Immelmann nearly six months to down seven Allied planes, while the great Boelcke downed only five in the same length of time. Since these two aces were the top men in Germany's Air Force, the inference that all Allied airmen were "Fokker

Fodder" before the front-firing Fokker monoplane, can hardly be accepted. The words "Fokker Fodder" made a convenient alliteration for postwar fiction writers.

Naval Aviation

Military aviation, as far as naval forces were concerned, flew a turbulent course as blue-water admirals wanted no part of the aeroplane. Few of them could see any value in the powered machine, and most of them pointed out that Germany, coming on as a great naval power, was content to allow Zeppelin crews to carry out what aerial reconnaissance might be attempted. As a result, the aerial gasbag, later known as the "blimp," was for some time accepted generally as an adjunct to naval power.

But only Germany was capable of efficient lighter-than-air operations, or in building airships that would fly, stay in the air for long periods of time, and to a great extent defy inclement weather. The British were particularly unfortunate in this field, while the French and Italians were little better off. However, before the war was over, both had developed some lighter-than-air equipment that was put to good use over the Mediterranean. In the United States, lighter-than-air operations were still in the hands of the country fair exhibitors. There was no official Army, or Navy, airship service after 1909. The year before the U. S. Army had accepted and flown a nonrigid airship. A handful of pilots were trained in the lighter-than-air art, and a few more were still experimenting with free and captive balloons from which they were taking aerial photographs or checking out radio reception.

America's first contribution to naval aviation was her interest in and development of aircraft-carrier operations, for someone with foresight had already realized the potential of the aeroplane, and suggested that it be mated in some manner with the surface ships. The flying boat and float plane were first considered for naval-air operations as they were capable of taking off and landing on the water; that is to say, they could under favorable conditions, but it was soon realized that if aircraft were truly to serve the Navy, special vessels would have to be designed to accommodate and service them.

There always were a number of handling problems connected with the frail machines of that era, problems that detracted from their practical value. They took up too much space aboard the tenders; they were difficult to handle aboard ship; to launch over the side or to retrieve after a patrol had been completed. Because of their weight and size these early machines were limited to scouting missions, although, as has been explained, one or two aircraft manufacturers had pondered on the torpedo-plane concept.

What Navy men wanted was a light, long-range aircraft that could defend itself, scout the enemy, take off from and land back on a mother ship; the last two qualities would save a tremendous amount of time, and, more important, allow the vessel concerned to keep station with its own flotilla or fleet. There would be no necessity to slow down to put the aircraft into the water or to pick it up again. With the increased speed of surface operations, this was of prime consideration. If an aircraft could be launched from a vessel of war while she was under way and brought back again under the same circumstances, the art of naval warfare could be vitally improved.

The Wright brothers had used a dropped-weight catapult to launch their early successful biplanes. This device produced one form of initial propulsion. The problem of a short-strip landing was solved partly by another American, Eugene Ely, a noted pilot of the Glenn Curtiss school who made the first carrier-deck landing and take-off. This was accomplished on January 19, 1911, while he was flying an early Curtiss *June Bug* biplane. Reconstructed versions of this historic plane have been seen at aviation meets in the past few years. It was powered with a 30-horsepower engine that twirled a 6-foot propeller. It was equipped with a tricycle landing gear.

Ely prepared for the display by wrapping a number of inflated bicycle tubes about himself. He took off from the Presidio in San Francisco and flew out to the USS *Pennsylvania*, a cruiser of that period, and landed on a short platform mounted over the stern of the deck. The Curtiss pilot approached the cruiser at about 40 miles per hour, and used a variation of today's hook-and-cable arrester equipment; a series of ropes with small sandbags tied at each end which were stretched across two wooden rails that ran lengthwise along the landing platform. Suspended a few inches high, the ropes caught and held the trailing hooks, and afforded the means of snubbing the forward speed, slowing down the plane, and restraining it to the short flight deck.

Later that day Ely's biplane was turned around, the ropes and sandbags removed, and he took off and flew back to the Presidio field. The landing-cable feature became the basis of today's very elaborate plane-snubbing system used by all naval carriers. But, unfortunately, the U. S. Navy did not pursue the venture, and the aircraft carrier, as such, was first developed and used in action by the British.

British naval aviation can be traced back to 1908 when a new post of Naval Air Assistant was established at the Admiralty, but it was not until 1912 that heavier-than-air machines were considered seriously for naval operations. The general attitude toward any proposed carrier operations is best illustrated by a statement that appeared in a London aviation journal that same year. It read:

"It is reported without any corroboration that Mr. (Lieutenant) Samson has the intention of alighting on the deck of one of our battleships at Sheerness. It is sincerely hoped that he will not make the attempt, for he is not only one of the most magnificent flyers in the country, but he is an exceedingly valuable officer and a man of considerable mental ability, and should not, therefore, be permitted to risk his life on what is, when all is said and done, simply a dangerous trick which though it may perhaps seem convincing to a few old-fashioned officers who do not yet realize even the present possibilities of the aeroplane, is actually of no practical value whatever."

But the young bloods of the Royal Navy had other views, and several stuck doggedly to their opinions, and disregarding a series of tragedies and mishaps involving the service's lighter-than-air craft, pushed their "impractical" plans with even more determination.

There were several reasons for this. On November 18, 1911, Commander Oliver Schwann made Britain's first successful take-off from the water while flying a 35-horsepower Avro biplane. The first United States float-plane flight had been made by Glenn H. Curtiss aboard a Curtiss hydroaeroplane at San Diego, California, on January 26, 1911, and Henri Fabre, a Frenchman, was the first airman to take off from the water when he performed this feat in 1910 aboard a *canard* machine in which the main planes were fitted to the rear of the body frame, and the engine mounted in what would be considered the center section.

Fabre straddled the upper main body member and sat facing the tangle of control surfaces. The floats were made of thin veneer and were formed into a hollow shape that was curved fore and aft much like the wings. They not only provided the lift from the water but also assisted in supporting the aircraft in the air. With this gear Fabre could take off from the water on these frail floats, but he had to land on a sandy beach or a grassy meadow.

The question arises: Was this the first amphibian plane?

The aforementioned Lieutenant Charles R. Samson of Great Britain flew a Short S.27 from an improvised deck built on the forecastle of HMS *Africa* while she was at anchor at Chatham, England—December 1, 1911—and made a safe descent alongside, using a set of air-filled torpedo-shaped flotation bags attached to the undercarriage and the tail. A month before Lieutenant A. M. Longmore had taken off from Eastchurch and made a successful landing in the River Medway with a comparable device. Lieutenant Samson continued these experiments all through the following spring, and during the Naval Review at Weymouth in May 1912 he took off from HMS *Hibernia* while she was steaming at 15 knots, and it is presumed that he again landed safely on the water nearby to be hoisted aboard. All these trials and experiments eventually changed the S.27 to the Short S.38/T.2, and it was used for naval training, experiments with wireless, and some attempts at mounting a machine gun for the observer.

At the same time the U. S. Navy which appears to have neglected the early success in deck take-offs, gave some attention to the prospects of catapult-assist take-offs. Several experiments were made along this line, but it was not until 1916 that an actual catapult, suitable for active-service conditions, was fitted to the USS *North Carolina*.

British naval aviation took another stride when a naval wing of the Royal Flying Corps was formed in 1912, and nautical problems seriously considered. By the end of that year the Royal Navy had sixteen aircraft in service, thirteen of which were land planes; only three were hydro-aeroplanes. That year also saw Lieutenant Samson drop a naval bomb from a Short S.41 biplane, and by the summer of the next year four shore stations, Calshot, Cromarty, Felixstowe, and Great Yarmouth were established.

An interesting feature of this period was the operation of two seaplanes from a wheeled launching platform mounted forward aboard HMS *Hermes*. One of these machines, a Short *Folder*, an aircraft in which the wings could be folded for shipboard stowage, was employed in the experiments. This plane became the forerunner of many carrier-based aircraft that were to be produced by Shorts and other manufacturers. A Short seaplane, known as the Type 166, was designed to carry a naval torpedo into the air. It was not completed until some time in 1914, and it is not known whether it actually carried such a weapon into the air. Some historians state that one was taken into the air and dropped, but the details are vague and undocumented.

All these experiments were interesting and afforded novel exhibitions for the Royal Navy, but the continued expansion of the German Navy was watched closely, and by July 1914 the Royal Naval Air Service had become an independent force with fifty-two seaplanes, thirty-nine land planes, seven airships of varying value, 128 officers, and 700 ratings (or enlisted men). As the threat of war spread ominous clouds over Great Britain during that memorable summer, the Grand Fleet was gathered at Spithead for the annual review that, on this occasion, was to cover five days —from July 18–22. On the twentieth an impressive flight of naval aircraft flew in a V over the fleet and gathered crowds, giving the first public exhibition of formation flying. Then came seventeen seaplanes, followed by four naval airships that cruised majestically above the review area.

This was the greatest display of "military" aircraft yet seen in Britain, and it must have been most impressive, as the precision of that early formation flying reflected the enthusiasm and skill of the adventurous men who flew those prehistoric machines. Because of the spirit and interest of the public, the planes in this display were dispatched on a tour of Great Britain, but, by the evening of July 27, were suddenly ordered back to their home stations. On the twenty-ninth the Cabinet advised the Admiralty that since the Royal Flying Corps, as the military wing was now called, would accompany the Army when it was engaged abroad, the Royal Naval Air Service would take over the responsibility for the air defense of Great Britain, and that these duties must take precedence over the purely naval requirements of patrol and scouting.

Thus began the Great War in which for the first time in history men were to stage great battles in the sky. On August 6, 1914, Harry Harper, who had seen so much of the development of the aeroplane, wrote his first air-war dispatch for the *Daily Mail*. It read:

"One of several German aircraft which flew over Liège was attacked by a Belgian war aeroplane which charged it at a height of 1500 feet and cut it in half. The heroic Belgian is said to have escaped alive. He is the first man to carry out the vow taken in the airman's camp to ram all hostile aircraft."

Acknowledgments

Without the generous assistance of many officials and organizations this work could not have been completed. I am deeply indebted to several officials of Her Majesty's Stationery Office in London from where much valuable information was obtained, and also to Otis H. Greeson of the National Museum of the Smithsonian Institution in Washington, D.C., who contributed many photographs, much data, and made several useful suggestions as to where other material could be obtained.

The Imperial War Museum of London furnished me with many excellent photographs, as did my good friend, Charles Cain of London. Lieutenant Colonel C. V. Glines, Acting Chief of the Magazine and Book Branch of the United States Department of Defense, kindly provided several important photographs produced in this book, as did the United States Navy's Office of Information. To all these cooperative and generous friends, I am most grateful.

Arch Whitehouse
Montvale, New Jersey
October 1964

Bibliography

Babington-Smith, Constance, *Testing Time*, Harper & Row, 1961.

Barber, H., *The Aeroplane Speaks*, Robert McBride & Company, 1917.

Brewer, Griffith, *50 Years of Flying*, Air League of the British Empire, 1946.

Burge, C. G., *Encyclopaedia of Aviation*, Isaac Pitman & Sons, 1936.

Duke and Lanchbery, *The Saga of Flight*, John Day Company, Inc., 1961.

Grahame-White and Harper, *The Aeroplane*, J. B. Lippincott Company, 1911.

Jane, Fred T., *All the World's Aircraft*, Sampson, Low, Marston & Company, 1909.

Kelly, Fred C., *The Wright Brothers*, Ballantine Books, 1943.

———, *Miracle at Kitty Hawk*, Farrar, Straus & Young, 1951.

Lewis, Peter, *British Aircraft 1809–1914*, Putnam and Company, Ltd., 1962.

Lougheed, Victor, *Vehicles of the Air*, Reilly & Britton, 1909.

Miller, Francis Trevelyan, *The World in the Air*, G. P. Putnam's Sons, 1930.

Payne, L. G. S., *Air Dates*, William Heinemann, Ltd., 1957.

Saunders, Hilary St. George, *Per Ardua*, Oxford University Press, 1945.

Wallace, Graham, *Flying Witness*, Putnam and Company, Ltd., 1958.

Index